LEGS

AN AUTHENTIC STORY OF
LIFE ON THE ROAD

OSCAR DEXTER
BROOKS

KEY PORTER•BOOKS

To my wife Hilda
who convinced me that a contributor's rewards
were greater than a taker's material gains

Canadian Cataloguing in Publication Data

Brooks, Oscar
    Legs

ISBN 1-55013-287-3

I. Title.

PS8553.R66T3 1991   C813`.54   C91-093090-2
PR9199.3.B76T3 1991

Key Porter Books Limited
70 The Esplanade
Toronto, Ontario
Canada M5E 1R2

Printed on acid-free paper
Printed and bound in Canada by John Deyell Company

91 92 93 94 95 6 5 4 3 2 1

GLOSSARY

balling the jack	speeding
B. and O.	Baltimore and Ohio railroad
banjo	shovel
benny	overcoat
big hook	big steam crane
bindle	bedroll
bindle stiff	tramp who carries a bindle
bitch	improvised candle
booming	going from one job to another
boston	pool game
bull cook	cook's helper
bundle team	pair of horses hitched to a wagon with five-foot-high wooden sides that hauls grain sheaves to the threshing machine
C. and A.	Chicago and Alton railroad
canned heat	wax soaked with alcohol (see "sterno"); lush who drinks canned heat
carry the banner	walk the street to keep warm at night when you haven't the price of a bed
case dough	the last of your bankroll
clam	one dollar
crummy	caboose
damper	cash register
derail or rubbydub	denatured or rubbing alcohol
deuce	two dollars
Eighteenth Amendment	U.S. law prohibiting the manufacture, sale, import and export of intoxicating beverages
fin	five dollars
fresno	a type of roadbed scraper drawn by a four-horse team (no connection to the city of Fresno)
gandy dancer	railroad track construction worker
gate	railway switch
goat	yard locomotive
harness bull	police officer

head end	Locomotive and Water Tender
hieser	tramp
highball	two whistle toots, signaling that a train is about to move
hit a lick	make a score
hogger	locomotive engineer
horse cock	bologna
jackrolling	robbing a drunk or a sleeping hobo
Johnson bar	a long pipe-like handle, part of a fresno (see "fresno")
jungle buzzard	tramp that scavenges food in the jungle
Kelly game, pea pool	pool game played with numbered peas
key men	skilled workers
knob-knocker	safe-cracker
lump	back-door food handout
M. and P.	Missouri Pacific railroad
mulligan pot	large can for cooking stew
pearl diver	dishwasher
punk	bread
redball	through freight train
rip-rapping	reinforcing the sides of a railroad cutting with stones
sawbuck	ten dollars
scissor bill	farmer
shack	brakeman
sky pilot	preacher
snake	switchman
stem	street or avenue
stemming	begging on the street
sterno	wax soaked with alcohol (see "canned heat")
taking the whiskers off	harvesting
tallow pot	fireman
tap city	broke
toppings	stale cakes, cookies, sweets
town clown	town cop
way freight	local freight train
wobbly	member of the Industrial Workers of the World
yard bull	railroad policeman

PROLOGUE

THERE WERE THREE OF US SITTING BESIDE THE creek in the aspen grove outside Cut Bank, Montana. The sun had just dropped behind the trees when we heard the rhythmic tap-dance of the passenger train as it sped toward the hobo jungle—then whooosh! And it was gone.

"Jesus," said one of the hobos, "that rattler's gotta be doin' ninety. Must be somethin' to ride the plush and use a tile can steada hangin' your ass out a boxcar door."

The bo that spoke was about eighteen. On his long blond hair sat an oversized fedora, once gray, now filthy. Only his jug-ears kept it from blinding him. With a bath and proper clothes he would have been handsome. But the beige windbreaker on his bony frame was far too small, leaving three inches of dirty wrists jutting from his sleeves, while the crotch of his pants hung halfway to his knees. He looked like an overgrown gnome.

The short, middle-aged guy beside him had a bulging belly and a growth of salt-and-pepper stubble. A cast in his left eye, accented by huge black eyebrows, gave him a sinister look. He sat on the ground with legs outstretched, resting his back on a bindle propped against a stump. "Yup," he said when the parlor-car disappeared, "on the plush, lad. But not on the head end. Ridin' them engines is a helluva way to get where yur goin'."

"What's the matter with the head end?" asked the kid. "It's a hell of a lot better'n these crummy way freights we been ridin'. I'm gettin' humpbacked from loadin' and unloadin' freight for the train crew just so's they won't kick us off. And where do we go? Forty or fifty miles a day, that's all. You ain't gonna get nowhere or see nothin' that way."

"What's there to see? The country and the people's all the same wherever yuh go. The poor'll give you a handout they can't afford, and the rich bastards look down their nose at you."

"I ain't denyin' about people," said the kid. "But that rattler'll be in Frisco tomorrow night, and where'll we be? I'll tell ya where we'll be—forty miles up the line, eatin' dry bread. At the rate we're goin' we ain't gonna get to the west coast till the snow flies."

"Well, we ain't gonna do nothin' in Frisco can't wait," said Evil Eye. "And let me tell yuh this, yur eatin', ain't yuh? And yuh sleep in a warm bindle every night? Can't figger out why yur so goddamn anxious to get to Frisco. There ain't nuthin' there 'cept cops and the Sally Ann. And if yuh go to the Salvation Army, yuh gotta listen to them Bible thumpers for three hours if yuh want a flop or somethin' to eat. I'll tell yuh this! If yuh were on that flyer yuh'd be half frozen and the only food yuh'd be puttin' in yur belly'd be cinders. No sir! They're not for me."

"Listen," said the kid. "If we was on that train we'd still have the bindle. All we gotta do is spread it out on the water tender and crawl in. What's a few cinders? They'll wash off."

Then the kid pulled a hunk of punk from a soiled brown paper bag and stuck it in his mouth, but took it out before he clamped his choppers on it. I thought he was going to throw it away, but after he scowled at it a while, he bit into it and chewed it slowly before gulping it down like a kid taking castor oil.

I had just finished lighting the fire under a piece of gravel screen resting on four stones when the train went by. Now the can of coffee water on the screen was boiling, and the ground beef I had in the pan was sizzling, giving off an odor that must have made the kid's dry punk seem drier. Evil Eye licked his lips.

"Sure must be nice to be in the chips and eat food like that, Mac," he said. "All we got is a sack of toppin's and dry bread."

I'm not a brainy guy. I'm just road smart. I've been traveling enough to be able to tell the pisspot from the handle, and I know a jungle buzzard when I see one. A good bum usually has more grub than he can eat and shares it with other bums in the jungle, but he hates to share it with a scavenger bum. A bum that won't rustle food for himself or the stew pot and hangs around the jungle drinking coffee seconds and eating the leavings of the mulligan pot is called a jungle buzzard and is scorned by the bos that hustle for themselves.

In my book Evil Eye was out on three called strikes. One, he was a bindle stiff, hated by every working stiff from L.A. to the big town because their bedrolls are always lousy, and they louse every camp they hire into. Two, I knew he was a wolf and going up the kid's rear, and wolves are my pet hate. Three, he was a jungle buzzard.

"You could eat good chow too," I told him, "if you ditched your girlfriend, got out and kicked your feet in the right places. Christ almighty! There's more people to bum than the baker. Take a shot at asking someone for something besides stale rolls and yesterday's bread."

"Yuh think yur pretty goddamn smart for a punk that hasn't stopped shittin' yellow yet," he snarled. "But I'll cure you of that if yuh keep flappin' that big lip of yurs." He got to his feet. Standing up he looked bigger. This made me leery but not scared.

"You got it wrong, bud," I said. "I don't think I'm smart. I am. I'll knock you on your ass so fast you'll think the ground's a magnet."

He squinted his bad eye. "I ain't about to fight yuh, but yuh got no call to be talkin' like that. No man has to take that from another man, and I ain't takin' it from no punk kid. An if yuh keep it up yur the one'll get the shit kickin', not me. I'll take care of that myself."

Figuring I'd won the round I clammed up and went to cooking. I threw a handful of coffee in the can of boiling water and left it for a minute before taking it off the fire. Then I poured a tin of cold water in it to settle the grounds. By this time the meat was cooked. I set it aside while I cut two slabs off the loaf of punk. While the meat was frying I was hungry enough to eat the shingles off an outhouse. But now I didn't give a damn whether I ate or not. The hassle with the wolf and watching the kid munching dry punk had stuck a nail in my appetite.

It reminded me of Winnipeg the first day I was alone on the road, hungry and broke. I'd been hungry before. Everyone misses a meal now and then, but sooner or later they know they'll eat, and there'll be food enough on the table to stuff their guts. Someone will feed you if you tell enough people you're broke and hungry. But I'm telling you this, and it's God's truth. If it hasn't happened to you, you don't know how hard it is to ask a stranger for a handout. But you'll do it, because hunger makes you. It will give you the guts to humble yourself and step up to a stranger as if you've known him all your life and put the beg on him, and if he doesn't feed you, you'll keep begging until you get fed.

Guilty with these thoughts I took the coffee pot and pan of meat to a stump beside the stream that ran through the jungle. Then I turned and looked at the kid staring at me with his eyes begging like a lost dogie in a swamp. His mouth was open, and I could see the half-chewed cud of white punk between his yellowed teeth. I took a bite, and when I did the kid gulped and swallowed the cud. Disgusted with myself for allowing my dislike for Evil Eye to keep me from sharing my ample meal with the kid and him, I stopped eating, put my fork down, picked up a lard pail lid, put some meat on it with two big slices of fresh punk, and held it out to the kid. I was going to offer the wolf some too, but before I could, he sprang to his feet and came at me with a club. "Leave the kid alone. I'm lookin' after him," he growled.

I knew I could take him with the dukes. I was young, over six feet and weighed one seventy-five—but there's no way I'd go against a club-wielding madman with my knuckles. If I couldn't get an equalizer, I'd take it on the heel and toe and get the hell away. But there was no reason to take the H. and T. I had an evener in front of me, and before he took two steps, I grabbed my shiv from the plate and set myself to meet him with my legs braced.

"Don't come any closer, you old fart," I said, brandishing the knife wildly. "I'll nut you so quick you'll think you were born gelded. You'll be talking high C for the rest of your life. I'm not after your boy. I don't swing that way, but I couldn't care less about what you and he do. It's his ass. He can haul coal in it for all I care. I was going to give you a hunk of meat too if you hadn't made a prick of yourself, and the offer's still there if you cool down and act like a man instead of a rooster."

The wolf hauled up fast and stood staring. "Yuh think the knife scares me? Yuh goddamn well better think some more. Takes a special kind to cut a man up, and yuh ain't the breed. Most people think it takes guts to carve a man. 'Tain't so. It takes meanness, not guts, and yuh ain't got neither. Tell yuh what. You drop the knife and I'll drop the club, and we'll fight man to man. Then yuh'll see who's the toughest. Yuh been on my ass since yuh first opened yur yap."

"On your ass? Whaddayamean I been on your ass? I call a spade a spade, that's all. If you can't take the flies get out of the bush. I'm not backing off a goddamn bit from what I said. If you want to eat, I'll feed you too."

After I said this, I turned my back on Evil Eye and tossed the shiv point down on the stump, where it quivered, ready to be snatched up if needed. Instinct made me turn back quickly in case I was wrong in thinking he would rather eat than fight—I wasn't going to be caught bare-assed—but he ran true to my figures. He'd tossed the club down and was on his way to his bindle to get something to eat off.

But still wanting the last word, he said, "So yuh'd rather feed us than fight? Then why'd yuh make all those smart-assed cracks? Why didn't yuh keep quiet and share yur grub? There ain't nuthin' gained by that kind of talk. What yuh say to me and I say to yuh don't carry no weight nohow. After tomorrow we'll prob'ly never see each other again. Yuh'll take one train and I'll take another, so why make a big to-do 'bout somethin' ain't none of yur business—and yuh can't prove?"

"Okay, I'll bury the hatchet," I agreed. "I said what I said because of the kid. Look at him, sitting there taking everything in and saying nothing. He's whipped. The road's got him beat. He can't cope. He's got to get off it before he's fucked for life. You wouldn't want that to happen would you? Or are you the kind of guy that doesn't care, as long as you get what you want? Why the hell don't you put him on a freight and send him home?"

"There yuh go again. Yuh gotta keep waggin' that fat tongue of yur'n. Why da yuh do that? Talkin' outta turn like yur always doin' must get yuh a lotta busted beaks and fat lips."

Getting riled up again didn't stop Evil Eye from pulling a filthy enamel plate from his bindle. Instead of taking the plate to the stream and scouring it, he rubbed it on the elbow of his coat sleeve and held it out to me. What the hell! This thing could go on all night, or till one of us got hurt. I replied in deeds not words.

"My peace offering," I said when I plunked a slab of ground beef the size of his hand on the plate, grabbed my knife and the loaf of punk, cut off two slabs and dropped them on the plate beside the meat.

To my surprise, before going back to sit on his bindle and eat he said, "Thank you."

I let him take a few noisy bites before I said, "You had the last word, but I agree with what you said before. We'll part tonight or tomorrow and not find out each other's names, or the part of the country we hail from. But just for the record, my friends call me Legs."

When I loaded the lard pail top with meat and bread and handed it to the kid, he said, "I ain't whipped, and I ain't goin' home. I'm goin' to Frisco to my uncle's. He'll get me a job in the pickle factory where he works. He's a foreman there. I'll go with you, Legs, and it won't take long, because you move. You don't piss around with way freights. You ride redballs and hold them down for three or four divisions before you unload. We been ridin' trains for three weeks and ain't rode a through freight yet. We'll never get to Frisco ridin' these crummy way freights."

But I had no intention of playing big brother. I snapped back, "Not me, kid. I'm a loner. I'm feeding you now, but taking you with me's not in the cards. I'll be long gone before you're up and around in the morning. Take my advice and go home. If you won't listen to good advice, do what you want—but not with me. I found out a long time ago it's easier to go it alone on the road. That way you're free as a fart in a breeze."

Disappointed and showing it, the kid went to a fallen tree, straddled it and sat down with the plate of grub between his thighs. Then, pulling a jackknife from his pocket, he cut a chunk off the meat. When he finally clamped his choppers on it, his sun began to rise. The satisfied gleam from his eyes in the firelight made me feel less like a bastard for rejecting his request.

No one talked while we ate. The kid finished first and made a show of mopping the lard pail lid with his last piece of punk and popping it in his mouth. Then he stood up, wiped his mouth with the back of his grimy hand, walked over to a tree and pissed against it. As he buttoned his fly, he said, "Okay, if I can't go with you, Legs, I'm goin' to catch the head end of the next passenger train going west, and I'll be in Frisco by the end of the week."

I filled three cans with steaming coffee before I said, "Your pardner's right. Those passenger trains are built for comfort, but you got to ride the cushions to get it. Riding up front is goddamn miserable. Why ride when you don't have to? Have you ever seen a tallow pot fill a water tender?"

"What's a tallow pot?" the kid asked.

"That's the fireman. I've watched hundreds of them and never saw one shut the water off before the tender overflows. The spout's at least twelve inches in diameter. With a gusher like that how long do you think it takes the overflow to cover the tender deck with an inch of water? The tallow pot don't give a damn if you get a wet ass or not. And if he's low on coal and needs a passer, you'll pass coal or get your ass kicked off the train fifty miles from nowhere. If you think muscling freight is tough, you'll change your thinking after you climb into a half-filled coal hopper and shovel coal in the slipstream of a big road hog barreling down the track with eight drivers a side."

I thought from the perplexed look on the kid's kisser I wasn't getting to him. I would have clammed up if he hadn't said, "You learned, and I can too."

Knowing he was listening wound me up again. "Take my word for it, riding the head end isn't what it's cracked up to be. You can't get off to eat or you'll miss the train, so you live on a diet of cinders from the time you climb aboard until you unload. Who the hell wants that?"

Instead of answering, the kid began to fidget, so I poured him and myself a coffee before carrying on. "You think I'm steaming off like a locomotive blowing down?" I said. "I'm not. I speak from experience. Do you know what'll happen if you grab a passenger out of here tomorrow? You're going to be working for the county for thirty or sixty days. Whether it's sixty or thirty will depend on which side of the bed the judge got out when he left the sheets the morning you go to bat. He won't give a damn about you or your uncle or the pickle factory. All he'll be interested in is protecting vested interest. Then, when you've done your time they'll load you in the sheriff's car and drive you four or five miles out of town and dump you on the road with orders not to come back. How do I know? Because I've been there. The yard bull's going to pick you off the train or grab you in the yards because you don't have the savvy to outsmart him."

When I finished, the kid bristled up. "I know you been around a lot more than I have and think I'm stupid. But I'm not, and I'm not goin' to get caught by the yard bull, because I can take care of myself. You don't have to be very smart to watch out for the yard bull. I'm fed up eatin' dry bread and not goin' anywhere, so what you said won't make me change my mind."

So the kid did have guts, and his show of moxie made me feel good. Maybe he'd make it after all. Maybe I put the figures on the kid too quick. Maybe I'd been too blunt. But maybe that's what he needed. Maybe a few square meals under his belt and a little encouragement would straighten him out.

But what the hell could I say and still keep him at arm's length? There was no way I was going to take him under my wing and look after him all the way to the coast. Still, to put him at ease I said, "Hell, man! I don't think you're stupid, but you can't learn much in three weeks. You may be a good farmer, but that don't make you a good bum. To get along on the bum you have to be a bit of a con man and that takes experience.

"Do you want to know what I told the butcher to get all that meat? I told him there was a hell of a plight in the jungle. There were six men in the jungle and they were all starving to death. I asked him if he could give us something for the pan, just anything at all, odds and ends, hooves or horns or an old bacon butt. He was a right guy. He laughed and pointed to a quarter of beef hanging on the meat rack and said, 'Unhook that quarter of beef and take it with you. At the rate I'm giving my meat away I'll be on the bum myself, so let me know when it's ready to eat, and I'll come down to help you eat it.' Then he slapped about three pounds of ground beef in waxed paper and gave it to me."

The kid grinned. "You won't have to look after me if I take a redball when you do. I'll just be on the same train, that's all, and that won't be no trouble to you, because you're goin' to take the train anyhow."

"You say you won't be any trouble. Goddamn it, kid! You spell trouble. Who's going to feed you and get you a flop at night? The first thing you have to do if you're going to stay on the road is get yourself some clothes that fit you. And you have to keep clean. That outfit you're wearing would scare Christ off the cross. You look like a Dickens character from the slums."

"It's easy for you to say, get better clothes," he sulked, "but where the hell am I gonna get better clothes with no money?"

"Nothing to it," I answered. "Go to a funeral parlor. There isn't an undertaker between here and the coast that doesn't have two or three outfits he'll give to charity or throw away. When they bring in a stiff with his clothes on, the first thing the undertaker does is undress the body. And before he puts it in the casket the dead guy's relatives bring in the stiff's best suit to put on the body, and they seldom pick up the old ones. It seems people have a horror about wearing clothes taken off a corpse."

The kid looked sick. "You're crazy," he said. "I'd rather have these and the lice than wear clothes off a dead man. I'll wear what I got to Frisco if I don't take all year to get there, and my uncle'll get me some new ones. I promise I won't be no trouble."

"Trouble or not, you're not coming with me. If you don't want to wear clothes off a dead man, get them anyway. Then you can pawn them in the first hock shop you come to and buy yourself a pair of jeans and a thousand-mile shirt. A thousand-mile shirt is a polka dot like the rails wear. You must have noticed nearly all the brakemen and conductors wear polka-dot shirts."

All the time the kid made his pitch to travel with me, Evil Eye sat on his bindle with his trap shut. But suddenly he piped up with a sneer, "How in hell's the kid gonna bum an undertaker for a new front when he can't even knock on a back door for a handout? He'd better stay with me till he can feed himself. Time enough then to think about goin' it alone."

"I ain't gonna learn nothin' from you," the kid shot back. "I been with you for three weeks and never learnt nothin' yet."

"That's cause yuh never tried. Yuh gotta screw up your guts and ask folks to help yuh. I been tryin' for three weeks to get you to tell people yur hungry and can they help yuh, but yuh always get tongue-tied and back out at the last minute. Like the fellow says, yuh gotta speak up for yurself. Way I feel right now I don't give a good goddamn what yuh do. Whether yur here when I wake up don't make no difference to me. For more'n a week all I been hearin' from you is when are we gonna grab a through freight, cause all yuh got on yur mind is yur uncle and the goddamn job in the pickle factory."

The kid seemed undisturbed by what he said and stayed behind when the wolf picked up his bindle to look for a place to sleep. I waited until Evil Eye had disappeared, then said, "Before the next train going west comes along, you've got to put the figures on what you're going to do. Getting by on the road is more than riding rails, finding a night's flop, and keeping your belly full. You have to stop and hole up every so often, or you'll be on the bum for life. And who the hell wants to do that? When I hole up I try to find a job I can be happy with, but I haven't found one yet. The only work I can do well is farming, skinning horses or mules and driving spikes on an extra gang, and I don't want any of those to be my life's work."

That seemed to shut him up for a bit. He sat in silence for a while, staring into the fire, drinking his coffee and looking thoughtful. The fire was getting low and I was ready for a little shut-eye, so I spread out my bedroll. The kid did likewise. He was still as quiet as a clam, but after a while I quit noticing anything as my eyes closed.

I woke up early, just before dawn, and saw that the kid was already up and had a fire lit and water boiling. I shared my coffee with him again, and when we were both warming up on the steaming brew, he finally let out with what was on his mind.

"I thought a lot about what you said last night," he began. "Thought so hard I didn't get much sleep."

It wasn't easy to look interested at that hour, but I tried. I must have succeeded because he went on with hardly a break.

"I'm like you," he said. "I don't intend to stay on the bum, and I won't if I can get to Frisco. I really do have an uncle who's a foreman in a pickle factory, and he told me he'd give me a job if I went out there. And I'll get there, too. Nothing's goin' to stop me. But you don't have to take me. I'll get there on my own."

I looked around and finally said, "The town's starting to come alive. Lights are coming on in the houses. Keep the fire going, and put on a pot of fresh coffee. I'll be back in a few minutes. I'm going to hit a couple of those early risers for some bread and eggs. There'll be a train stopping for water in an hour, and we don't want to ride out of here on an empty gut."

We made San Francisco. And the kid's uncle did work in a pickle factory.

I'd met plenty of guys before who didn't seem cut out for the life of a bo, but not many who were so quick to figure out they'd be better off somewhere else. I'd been riding the rails myself for three years, working when I could and surviving by my wits when I couldn't, and I hadn't made my mind up yet.

CHAPTER 1

I TOLD THE KID HE DIDN'T HAVE ENOUGH ROAD smarts to get by, but I hadn't been any better myself when I first lit out from home. I took off with a friend who'd been on the road for two years and knew the ropes—and three days later, we were both in the can.

My father died when I was a toddler, and my mum in 1920 when I was thirteen. I went to live with my Aunt Susan and Uncle Orly on a farm in Saskatchewan. Their farm, like their family, was large— six boys and four girls. When the boys were old enough, Uncle Orly took them out of school to work on the farm, and by my uncle's reckoning I was big enough to work in the fields with my cousins.

Before I arrived my two oldest cousins had taken off to work, for pay, for other farmers. Two other boys left in the spring, making the workload heavier for the three of us remaining. I was big and strong for my age and didn't mind working from sunup till sundown for my keep. But I hated working my ass off and getting daily reminders about how ungrateful I was when I knew that I could do less work for strangers and get the going wage.

On Saturday night when the chores were done, my cousins and I saddled horses and went to town, each with a buck and a half given to us by big spender Uncle Orly. We'd spend the night in the pool room—my cousins playing, me watching. I would have liked to play too, but I was trying to get a bankroll saved to take it on the lam. I wasn't piling it up very fast, though, because we always went to the café before going home, and I'd often have to pay the tab because my cousins had spent their dough playing pool.

Three months before my fifteenth birthday, Uncle Orly hired Bert Mercer to help put the crop in. A tall, broad-shouldered eighteen-year-old, Bert had a sharp mind and an outgoing personality, and they had enabled him to adapt quickly to life on the road, and he'd boomed from one job to another for two years. Bert was just one of a whole army of itinerant workers who met the need for labor of the growing west. In those days, much of the planting, harvesting, timber cutting, road building, railway-track laying, and so on, was done by casual laborers. Men, many in their teens or early twenties, with a capacity for hard work and a touch of wanderlust, caught the freights and criss-crossed the land, living rough in hobo jungles when they had to, and hiring on to road gangs or timber crews, as farmhands or snow shovelers, wherever they heard there was a job going. It was a way of seeing the country and learning about life for a young man with a sense of adventure.

Bert and I hit it off, and when my night's chores were done I'd sit with him on the bunkhouse steps listening to his tales about jungles, yard bulls, and straw bosses in camps where he'd worked. And every time I heard a new story, my yen for the road grew. That's why, when the last seed was in the ground and Bert was leaving in the morning, I asked if I could go too.

This took Bert by surprise. He gave it some thought before he said, "You better think it over. Booming's a tough racket, you're working one day and on the bum the next. It's tough enough for a man to get by, and you're not fifteen yet. I know you're big for your age, and I know you can do a man's work, but I was older than you when I left home, and I had a hell of a rough time getting by before I got smart. Everybody you work for and every tramp in the jungle takes advantage of you. Sleep on it, and if you still want to go in the morning, it's okay with me."

"Then it's set. I don't have to do any thinking. That's all I've thought of since I got here, and all hell ain't going to make me change my mind," I said. "If I don't go with you I'm going alone."

"Then you better tell your uncle tonight that you're leaving, because I'll be gone before anyone's up. It's more than an hour's hike to Leney, and I want to catch that freight we see every morning when we head back from the barn to breakfast. I want to get into Saskatoon in time to catch a drag to Winnipeg in the afternoon."

"To hell with that. I'm not telling anyone. There'll only be a hassle if I do. I'll wind up getting talked out of going. It's better if I just take off and write them a note when I get a job."

"I don't care how you do it, but I don't want to wake everybody up crashing around in the dark to get you out of the sheets.

Whatever you're taking with you, pack tonight. Then get to sleep, because it'll be four o'clock before you know it."

For something to pack my gear in, I took a lead line with me when Bert and I left the barn. Then, after I told him not to worry about my sleeping in because I was going to stay awake until it was time to leave, I went to the granary and got a white cotton grain bag. Back in my room, I cut the lead line to make shoulder straps for the bag. Then I unscrewed the brass ball off the bedpost, where I'd stashed my getaway stake. It wasn't much of a stake, considering how long it had taken to hoard it. But when I stuffed the fourteen singletons in my hip pocket and knew when the sun rose I'd be gone, I wouldn't have traded my lot for a millionaire's.

When the bag was packed and ready, I flattened out on the bed with my clothes on. Bert had said he was fed up booming from one job to another and was going to Chicago to get a job in a factory. If I lied about my age I could get one too, he said. It was past my bedtime, but thoughts of living and working in America's second-largest city kept me awake. In my imagination, I visited many places I'd heard or read about in Hub Town: the Loop with its towering buildings and theaters, the elevated railway, and the long piers with their Great Lakes cargo ships.

Habit, though men and women at times are reluctant to admit it, is a compelling force; when resisted, like a malicious shrew, it nags, scolds and irritates until it wins its point. By midnight, my habit of early to bed, early to rise was pouring sand in my eyes. To stay awake I got off the bed to pace the floor. But then I realized my pacing would wake my aunt, who would wake my uncle, who would lose no time finding out why I was up.

I took out my dollar pocket watch, and struck a match to see the dial. When I saw it was only ten past midnight I knew I was in trouble. The only solution was to sneak out of the house as quietly as I could. With my improvised packsack on my back and my shoes in my hands, I crept stealthily downstairs and out the back door to the bunkhouse, where I shucked the pack and used it as a pillow when I went to sleep on the porch.

When Bert woke up, pulled on his pants and padded barefoot to the washbasin on the porch, he tripped over me. He'd have taken a header onto the ground if he hadn't grabbed the rail. I felt the jolt, but I went right back to sleep.

Bert washed before he shook me awake and said, "I'll be pulling out in ten minutes. If you're coming you better get your ass off the floor and have a wash. Why the hell didn't you use one of the bunkhouse beds? Sleeping in front of the bunkhouse door when you knew I'd be coming out in the dark is like setting a windfall trap for a bear. I damn near broke my neck."

"I'm sorry about that, but I wasn't taking any chances of your not seeing me."

This brought a chuckle from Bert, while I, still half asleep, went to the basin, filled it to the brim, and doused my head in the cold water. My antics changed Bert's chuckle to laughter, and he said, "Watch it, boy. Don't drown yourself. I don't want to hang around here another week waiting for the good people of the town to bury you."

Bert's good humor and the cold-water dunking revived me enough to reply, "Don't worry about that. I've waited two years for this day. I'm not going to blow everything by drowning myself. I'm wide awake now and ready to hit the trail."

When I followed Bert into the bunkhouse and was waiting for him to get dressed, a twinge of conscience hit me for not being man enough to tell my aunt and uncle I was striking out on my own. So I decided to leave them a note thanking them for looking after me. Having no paper or pencil I asked Bert if he had any handy. He fished a stub of a pencil from his jacket pocket, pointed to an envelope lying on the table and said, "This is the best I can do. Use that envelope, but make it short. It's time we were on the road."

Day was breaking when we got to Leney, but the town was still asleep. Bert said, "We're early, but that's better than being late. We can't even get a coffee in this one-horse town, so we might as well go up the track out of sight. You can catch up on your sleep while we wait for the train."

I was all for going up the track out of sight, but not to sleep. I said, "I'm too excited. I'm wound up tighter than a bull's ass in fly time.

My stomach feels like I swallowed a fifty-pound block of ice. I don't give a damn how sleepy I get today, I'm not going to sleep. I'm filing this day in my memory bank for all time. No matter what happens from now on, whether it's good or bad, May 17, 1922, is a day I don't ever intend to forget. But the sooner we get up the tracks out of sight the better. I need a piss so bad, but I don't want to piss on the town my last day here."

Bert looked up the tracks and said, "Christ almighty! The yard's bare as an apple tree in December. There's not a boxcar, tanker or gondola on the siding. The only place where we can get out of sight is behind that pile of ties past the section house."

Bert shucked his pack, and by the time I was buttoning my fly he was stretched out on the ground, using it for a pillow. I sat beside him and kept peeking around the tie pile, hoping to spot the train. Bert was lying on his back, watching the small, white, misty clouds chase each other across the gray-blue sky. I didn't know my nervousness was bothering him until I got up to piss for the third time. Then he said, "For Christ's sake, kid, sit down and relax. You've been up and down more times in the last twenty minutes than a whore's drawers on pay night in a bush camp. The train'll come. Fussing around like a hen with a brood of chicks ain't going to make it come any faster. You'll hear it before you see it. Sit down or lie down, and stop jumping up and down like a jumping bean."

What Bert said shook me up. The last thing I wanted to do was piss him off to the point he'd pull out on me the first chance he got. After I apologized I said, "Maybe a smoke'll calm me down. Give me the makings and I'll try it."

This put a smile on Bert's kisser.

"That won't help you," he said. "To get any good out of smoking you have to inhale. To prove it I'll roll you one, because I don't think you can."

"Go ahead, make one. I have to get rid of the shakes, and I'll inhale if I have to."

Bert rolled two cigarettes, lighted them and gave me one with the caution, "Take a small drag or you'll choke and cough your goddamn head off."

Cocky as hell, I stuck the cigarette in my mouth and took a medium drag. When the smoke hit my windpipe my face caught fire. My eyes began leaking tears the size of raindrops, and when the smoke filled my lungs I coughed and wheezed like a consumptive.

Bert waited until the spasm stopped. Then, amused, he pointed at my face and said, "For Christ's sake, kid! When I tell you something why don't you listen? Your face is redder than a drunk's nose. Try again, but this time do like I say. If you're going to take drags like a road hog with the blower on you better forget about smoking for now."

I should have taken Bert's advice and butted the cigarette, but my bullheaded pride wouldn't let me. I inhaled a tiny wisp of smoke and with an effort never choked. And when the irritation passed I took another and kept at it until I began to get lightheaded and a little dizzy. But as I'd hoped, it calmed me enough to be able to sit quietly beside Bert until we heard the blast of the big road hog's whistle.

The water tank was about two hundred yards west of the pile of ties, and when the fireman was taking on water we saw there were only four boxcars in the long string of gondolas and tankers, and they were at the rear, next to the caboose.

"Looks like an open-air ride," Bert frowned. "Those boxcars are too close to the crummy."

"What's the crummy?" I asked.

"That's the caboose. They're probably loaded anyway. We'll grab a gondola. It's better than the running board of a tanker this time of the year when the weather's not so hot. We'll be warmer in the gondola."

The train left slowly. We let a dozen cars go by before leaving the pile of ties and climbing into a gondola, where we sat without talking until the train was balling the jack. Then Bert spoke.

"I'm not going to run off at the mouth like a schoolmarm. And I don't want you to get the idea I'm getting ready to take a powder. We could get split up without being able to do a goddamned thing about it. Sometimes a yard bull or a town clown—that's a town cop—gets pissed off with one of two hobos he's collared and locks him up and not the other, or a smart-assed judge gives one bo time and not his buddy, because he wants to break them up. There's some things you need to know, and I may not be around to tell you. I watched you boarding the train. See if you can figure out what you did wrong."

I tried to think what I did different from Bert when I boarded the train but couldn't. "Nothing," I answered. "I did the same things you did."

"You think you did, but you didn't. You got on the rear of the car, and I got on the front. That may not seem important to you, but it could be the difference between life and death, or whether or not you spend the rest of your legless life peddling pencils on a street corner. Today it didn't matter because the train was crawling when we caught it. But it's dangerous when the train's going fast, or a little faster than you can run. You get a hell of a pull on your arms, and if you lose your grip you'll get thrown. And when the train throws you, its momentum swings you toward the tracks. If that happens and you've caught the rear end of the car, you'll wind up under the wheels. But if you've caught the front end you'll get swung against the side of the car, and instead of losing your life or limbs, you'll wind up on the ground beside the train, or in the ditch, less a few patches of skin."

Soaking up what Bert was telling me dampened my fervor until the government elevators and few tall buildings of Saskatoon loomed on the horizon, generating another wave of nervous excitement like my Leney attack. Having experienced the calming effects of nicotine, I asked Bert again for the makings.

He smiled, pulled the papers and tobacco from his smock pocket and was offering them to me when he had second thoughts. "You better let me roll it for you," he said.

In those days—and I haven't changed for the better—I learned everything the hard way. Not knowing Bert was trying to keep me from embarrassing myself, I said, "No, it looks easy. I'll roll it myself."

So he handed me the tobacco and papers. Thirty seconds later, my cockiness got a boot in the ass. I crumpled the torn cigarette paper and dropped it on the floor with the tobacco I'd spilled. Handing the tobacco sheepishly to Bert I said, "I guess you better roll it after all."

He chuckled and held up his hand. "No. You make it yourself. It's easy."

To save what face I could, I tried again, more carefully this time, and managed to roll a cigarette that bulged in the middle like an Adam's apple. The ends were skinny and tapered, but I knew it would smoke. I asked Bert for a match. He looked at the butt when I stuck it in my mouth and handed me a match with a laugh. "That's the first time I've seen a knocked-up smoke since I was learning to roll myself. Hell, man, it might birth before you get it lit. Hurry up or it might have twins."

I laughed with Bert, took a small drag of smoke, and inhaled it without coughing. And when I took another with the same success, I was too pleased with myself to worry about the Saskatoon yard bull.

At Saskatoon, we had no sweat getting off the train. It crawled into the yards because there was a westbound freight on the main line waiting for the Saskatoon train to clear the track west. Its head end shack stood beside the gate he'd opened to switch the incoming train onto a side track. When the crummy of the train cleared the main line, the shack would close the gate and highball his hogger west, and when the cab of the engine reached him, he'd climb aboard.

We left the train outside the yard and walked up to the shack tending the switch. Bert asked him if he knew when there was a train leaving Saskatoon for Winnipeg. He didn't, but told us to go to the roundhouse and ask someone there or look on the call board. We thanked him and walked toward the roundhouse until we were out of earshot. Then Bert stopped. "To hell with the roundhouse for now," he said. "We'll go there later if we have to. It's not good to go prowling around the yards when a train comes in. The bull's usually on the lookout for bos that might have been on the train."

Uptown we went to a Chinese café and made up for the breakfast we missed at Aunt Susan's table earlier in the morning. And after we put away a bowl of mush, then ham and eggs with home fries and toast, and were drinking a second coffee, Bert pulled out his makings, put enough tobacco in a cigarette paper to roll a smoke for himself, then pushed the tobacco and papers across the table to me.

"This time," he grinned, "don't put so much tobacco in the middle of the paper."

"No thanks," I said. "I don't need a smoke. I'm not nervous now. If I tried to roll a smoke in here, I'd give everyone in the joint a laugh at my expense." I pushed the papers and weed back to him.

CHAPTER 2

BERT PAID FOR HIS BREAKFAST BEFORE ME, AND went outside while I was paying for mine. I bought a tin of Tucket's Fine Cut and papers, which I showed him outside. "Now I don't have to bum from you, and I can roll some for practice on the way to Winnipeg."

He smiled and said, "Good, but I don't see any matches."

Abashed by my stupidity, I turned to get some. Bert stopped me. "Come on, I was only setting you up for a laugh. Hell, man, I got enough matches to last us till we reach Chicago."

When we were almost in the yard, Bert said, "There hasn't been a train go through since we got here, so it's not likely we'll run into the yard bull. If we do, he'll probably only ask us where we're going and where we're from. Then he'll tell us he'll run us in and charge us with trespassing if he catches us on railway property again."

Heading for the roundhouse we spotted a train crew making a train up. It meant nothing to me until Bert said, "We're in luck. We don't have to go to the roundhouse. We'll ask a snake about the train. They know as much about outgoing trains as a call boy. And before you ask me what a snake is, it's a switchman. They're good people, and will often tell you if the yard bull is on the prowl, and the best place to go to catch a drag leaving the yard." We walked up to a snake standing by a switch, and Bert asked him when there was a train going east.

He said, "Twelve-thirty if the goddamn hogger'll get the lead out of his ass and we get this train made up on time. It was supposed to be out of here at 11:20 a.m., but the goat blew a soft plug and we had to get another engine. We're nearly done, so I guess it'll get out of here by then. But you better get the hell out of the yard. The bull's on the prowl. A carload of whisky was broken into last night, and thieves made off with half a car of imported Scotch. You've got lots of time to bypass the yard and get to the main line. Wait there until the train pulls out."

We skirted the yards and were climbing over the wire fence that bordered the main line when we heard the two highball whistle blasts, then the clashing and clanging sounds of the couplings tightening between the cars when the hogger took slack.

The tallow pot had the blower on, and it made the smokestack belch a column of thick sooty black smoke that drifted over the cars like a storm cloud. We stood watching the big locomotive struggle to get under way, picturing the hogger pouring sand to give the engine's driving wheels traction and stop them from spinning until it gained enough momentum to haul the long string of loads without help.

We climbed over the fence and stayed there until the locomotive, still straining hard, went chuffing by at about four miles an hour. Then we hurried to the track and waited for an unsealed boxcar. When one came I trotted behind Bert as he kept pace beside it and unlatched the door. Then he grabbed the handhold at the bottom of the door, reefed it open and, without shucking his pack, clambered into the car. When he cleared the door I followed.

Bert was closing the door when I said, "Don't close it. I'd like to sit for a while and watch the scenery go by."

He left the door open, but gave me a disparaging look. "That's another thing you have to learn. A hobo that stays out of sight gets along better than one that don't. Not many train crews bother a hobo that's smart enough to stay under cover when he's beating his way. But all train crews get a mad on when scenic bums put themselves on display for the natives of every town the train goes through. In fact the crews not only boot scenic bums off the train, but usually wait until they take the hole for a meet with another train."

"What's that mean?" I asked.

"It means the side track. And the side track is not the only thing the train leaves behind when it gets back on the main line. It also leaves the scenic bum stranded there thirty miles from nowhere."

"Does that mean we'll be sitting in the dark all the way to Winnipeg?"

"Hell, no. You don't have to close it tight to stay out of sight. You leave it partly open. If you close it tight the shack might see it's unlatched and latch it when he's walking from the crummy to the head end when the train's in the hole. If it's partly open he'll probably not close it, because most doors are hard to close and he doesn't want the aggravation. Anyway, if he starts to close it you have time to let him know you're in there. It doesn't seem much, but guys have been locked in boxcars and damn near starved to death before somebody came along and found them. You don't have to be a scenic bum to see all there is and still stay out of sight."

I nodded. Then Bert closed the door to his satisfaction, went to the front of the car and lay on the floor with his head on his packsack.

Gazing at the moving panorama framed in the door's thin slit, I experienced strange thoughts and feelings. I wanted to leave this bleak, treeless land, with its short, hot, dry summers and long snowbound winters. I wondered what magnetic force attracted and held people here, working from sunup to sundown to scrape a living from their land when other places offered better climates, and easier ways to make a living. Now as I looked through the crack I was getting answers.

Before, when I looked at the plowed prairie fields I saw only a place where men and horses toiled, but now they had beauty. The vast expanse of tilled black loam became the background for scattered farmhouses and barns painted in many colors at the whim of each farmer or his wife; windmills in the barnyards, some pumping water, some idle; oases of trees planted around gardens, interspersed with green pastures; and brown, dissecting roads thrown in for contrast.

Visionary scenes formed, and they had beauty too. The planted wheat was now above the ground and had reached its early or "shot blade" growth, masking the black background with a sea of green wheatstalks rippling in the late-spring breeze. Then fall sneaked into the scene, bringing with it an ocean of golden, billowing, ripened wheat. And finally winter stormed in with a blanket of snow and turned the whole world white.

A hand on my shoulder broke the reverie. Startled, I turned. I hadn't heard Bert when he came up behind me. "For Christ's sake, kid," he said. "You been staring out that door without moving so much as an eyelash for twenty minutes. But I bet I know what's on your mind. You're having doubts about leaving home. Everyone does. Now get the hell away from that door and think about something else. It'll pass. It always does." Then without waiting to hear what I'd say or do, he went back and stretched out again.

I stood where I was and watched Bert lie down again before I followed him to the front of the car and sat on my packsack.

"If I was having second thoughts about leaving," I said, "I didn't know it. But it's strange how the prairie looked so beautiful. I started remembering what it looks like every season."

"Yeah, strange," Bert said, "but not so hard to figure out. You got a touch of nostalgia. Everyone on the road gets a touch of it now and then, but I'm surprised it hit you so soon. Roll yourself a smoke. It'll take your mind off home and you'll feel better. I'll roll one for you, if you like."

"No thanks. I gotta learn to roll them for myself, but have one on me," I said, taking the tin of Tucket's and papers from my pocket and handing them to him. I had less trouble rolling the cigarette than I had on the train to Saskatoon, but by the time I had it rolled and asked Bert for a light, his fag was half smoked.

When I boasted that morning in Leney that there was no way I'd spend any part of May 17th sleeping, I'd had no doubt about it. But I hadn't counted on falling asleep from inactivity, which I did. We were lying on the floor gabbing and smoking, when Bert raised himself on his elbow, butted his fag on the floor, lay down again, yawned and said, "I don't know how you feel, but I'm going to stop shooting the shit and get some shut-eye, and you should too." And before I stubbed my butt out he was snoring.

I was having more trouble staying awake fifteen minutes after Bert went to sleep than I had the night before on the bunkhouse porch and, without the same need to stay awake, I dozed off.

When I came to, the train was stopped, and Bert was staring out the door. Still sleepy, I would have gone back to sleep if my curiosity hadn't been stronger. "Where are we?" I asked. "What are we stopped for?"

Bert drew his head back and looked at me with a wry grin on his kisser. "Aren't you the guy that was going to celebrate his first day of freedom by staying awake until midnight? We're fifty miles east of Saskatoon, and we've been here half an hour. We got a meet with a westbound train, and it looks like a saw-by. Because we've left part of our train on the main line."

"Saw-by! What the hell's a saw-by?"

"It's the way two trains get past one another on a single track main line when the side track is too small for either train to take the hole and clear the main line. That's why the front end of our train is in the hole and the rest of our train is on the main line—but far enough west of the side track we're on to allow the other train to pass the siding and clear the main line. Then the front end of our train will pull onto the main line and go far enough east for the other train to hook onto the tail end of our train, haul it into the hole and leave it there. Then it backs onto the main line again and continues west. Meanwhile our train'll back into the hole, pick up the tail end and head east."

Bert was pissed off because it was after five o'clock before we got under way. "I should have my ass kicked," he snorted, "for not picking up a lump for the train."

Here we go again, I thought. Ever since we left Leney, every time Bert told me anything about the road, he used jargon. And I had to ask him to explain. I was hesitant about asking him what a lump was while he was in a huff, but anxious to learn the idiom of the road. I gambled: "What the hell's a lump?"

"Usually it's a handout you get when you bum a house, or a hunk of horse cock—that's bologna—or a loaf of punk you get from putting the rigging on a butcher or baker. But we're packing now and don't have to bum. We'd be eating now if I'd have bought something to eat on the train, and I would have if I hadn't been so sure the feed we had in Saskatoon would hold us till we got to Melville. I never figured on sitting in the hole for an hour waiting for a meet, and a saw-by at that."

Hungry or not we were both asleep when the sun went down, and when I woke up the inside of the boxcar was blacker than an undertaker's boot. "You awake, Bert?" I asked, loud enough to be heard over the clackety-clack of the wheels—except the train had stopped. No answer. I crept the two yards to where Bert was sleeping when I dozed off. When I fanned nothing but air I panicked.

Goaded by panic, and not thinking clearly, I sprang to my feet. I had taken off my boots before going to sleep, and Bert told me to tie the laces to a buttonhole of my fly. "You never know," he said, "when some petty-larcenous tramp might see the car partly open and climb in, spot a good pair of kicks on the floor beside a sleeping hobo and climb out again with the boots. And you'll have to sock-foot it until you bum or buy another pair."

Now, when I jumped up, the shoes dangling from my fly banged my knees like wrecking balls. In the dark I thought someone was kicking me. The thought shifted my heart into the big notch and started it thumping in my chest. To free myself from the unknown attacker I stepped back and discovered no one was there but my boots.

I was untying them and sorting things out when the brake cylinders began to bleed and the hogger highballed. We were taking off. I was on my own and had to make a snap decision—my first since I hit the road. Bert had gone. No time could be wasted wondering why. Chicago was out. I couldn't make it there on my own. Could I get a job in Winnipeg? Not likely. I had no skill to sell. All I knew was farming. The crop was in and they wouldn't be hiring until haying started in three weeks. Still, I was better off here than in Winnipeg. I'd get off the train when the car left the yards and stretch my bankroll till haying began or go hungry.

I shouldered my pack and was opening the door when I heard footsteps pounding the gravel ballast. Thinking it might be the yard bull I backed into the shadows, but stayed near the doorway and got whacked by Bert's packsack when it flew though the door. Then Bert's head and shoulders appeared at floor level outside the door, running alongside. He stuck a paper bag inside the boxcar. I can't say how happy I was to help him clamber aboard.

My excitement was such that while giving Bert a hand I blurted out, "Christ, man! When I woke up and found you gone and the train highballing outta the hole I damn near panicked. Where the hell'd you go?"

"I went for a lump and didn't want to wake you. I never woke up either when we took the hole, but the westbound train's whistle from a coupla miles out woke me."

"I was just getting ready to unload as soon as we left the hole," I said, "when I heard you running outside. Boy, am I glad to see you. But what you got in the bag? I'm hungry enough to eat a skunk's tail."

"Not a hell of a lot. The old boy had no bread, so we'll have to settle for crackers, sardines, horse cock and cheese. Too bad you weren't with me. You'd a got a belt out of the look on the old geezer's kisser when I walked into his store. It's the only store near the yard, and I'm sure he gets the rigging put on him nearly every time a train takes the hole here. He was sitting on the counter, gabbing with two oldtimers about crops, comparing this spring to 1912, the record crop of all times. But I broke up their gabfest and asked if anybody was minding the store."

"Christ almighty, Bert!" I said. "I wish you'd woke me up. I thought you got pissed off and ducked out on me. When I heard the train start to highball, I nearly crapped."

But Bert just kept rambling on as if I hadn't said anything. "The old guy hopped down like a two-year-old colt and asked, 'You got the wherewithal to pay for what you want? Most of the fellows going through here on freights expect me to give them something for nothing. Sometimes I do and sometimes I don't. Today I don't. A person's got to draw the line some time, or he'll be on the tramp himself.'

"For answer I whipped out my bankroll," Bert continued. "The old boy's eyes bugged when he saw my wad, and he bustled around getting me what I asked for."

"For Christ's sake, Bert," I said, picking up the bag and shaking it. "Cut the crap and let's open the bag."

Bert smiled. "God it's dark," he said. I can't see what the hell I'm doing, but I'll goddamn soon fix that. We'll eat by candlelight."

At last, he pulled out a hunk of bologna, unwrapped it and kept the string in his teeth while he opened two sardine tins. He scooped the sardines onto the waxed paper the bologna was wrapped in, then poured the oil from one tin into the other. Then he folded the string to a three-inch length, twisted the strands together and dropped it in the oil. Finally he pulled half an inch of oil-soaked string above the rim of the tin, put a match to it and grinned: "There's nothing better than a bitch to give a boxcar a homey feeling on a dark night. Now we'll eat in style."

Bert's crack about the cosiness of the bitch was not far off the mark. A small comfort is better than none.

The boxcar, though admittedly not a Pullman, gave me the comfortable, contented feeling I missed at my uncle's. And the glow from the bitch Bert fashioned in the darkness of the boxcar on that starless night must share part of the lure that kept me on the road for three years.

We were lying on the floor with our heads on our packs enjoying a smoke, when the flame of the bitch flickered and died. Bert butted his fag and said, "I'm going to catch some shut-eye, and you better get some sleep too, because with a little luck we'll be having breakfast in Portage la Prairie. Otherwise you'll be eating bacon and eggs with your eyes closed."

I tried to keep my tongue from clacking and go to sleep, but excitement and the hard floor kept me awake. Thinking Bert was having the same problem I kept firing questions, which he answered patiently, until I made a crack about how roadwise he was and got rebuked.

"Yeah, and if you keep asking questions and I keep answering them, by the time we get to Chicago you'll know as much as I do, but I'll be frazzle-assed from lack of sleep."

The rebuff dampened my ardor, buttoned my lips and kept them buttoned. Before my pride stopped smarting I was asleep, and I slept until the train crawled into the yard at Portage la Prairie.

Bert seemed none the worse for wear from his night on the hard floor, but I had a few sore spots and needed a cold wash to get the sleep out of my eyes. I was glad when he said, "We can stay on the train until it passes the roundhouse or stops, whichever comes first, because the bull's a right guy. All he'll do if he finds us is kick us out of the yards with a warning to stay out."

We got off the train near the roundhouse, and the only person we saw before getting to the roundhouse to wash was a car knocker—a journal inspector—waiting to work the train over. He told us it would be at least two hours before the train pulled out for Winnipeg.

Coming back to the yard after putting the feed bag on, we heard a ruckus at the stock pens. "What the hell's going on over there?" I asked.

"Hard to say," said Bert, "but we got time to kill. Let's find out. From the racket they're making I'd say it's a gang of men trying to load pigs." Bert called it like it was, only the gang turned out to be only two fat bewhiskered old geezers trying to load a pen full of squealing pigs into a cattle car. They had long pointed prods and knew how to use them. But two things were against them: their age, and the stubbornness of the pigs they were trying to drive up the ramp.

The two old bucks were trying to outshout the squealing pigs, and the pigs were trying to outsqueal the men, and the outcome was a cacophonous stalemate. If a pig broke rank it got a belt on the snout with the prod, and a lagging pig got a blood-drawing poke in the ass that made it squeal louder—which made the other pigs scream as if they'd been punctured too.

Looking through the opening of the plank palings was like watching a three-ring circus from the cheap seats, so we climbed the fence and sat on top.

In a drove of pigs, as in most animal gatherings, there are rebels whose ideas clash with those of authority. Like all dissidents, the rebel pigs had a sense of timing. They'd feign submission until the old men became lax, then dart from the drove and incite the docile pigs, who'd scatter all over the pen. And the old bucks would have to start over again.

We enjoyed the show until the men began to tire. Twice they nearly had the pigs in the chute, but both times a rebel pig ignored the clouts on his snout and broke rank, starting another stampede.

I knew if we helped them they could get the pigs in the chute, and it made me realize how callous we were, sitting on the fence like kids at a circus watching clowns perform and enjoying it.

"Let's get out of here," I said. "We should get a boot in the ass for sitting up here laughing at those two old geezers instead of giving them a hand."

"Yeah, you're right. Don't think I never thought about going down and helping them, but I didn't want to run around in pig shit. It would take an hour to get it off our boots, and there's always a chance you might slip. If you fall on your ass in that pen you'll come up smelling, and not of roses."

Twenty minutes later the train pulled out for Winnipeg. We were on it.

CHAPTER 3

I WAS DISAPPOINTED WHEN BERT DECIDED TO GO TO the jungle in Winnipeg and not uptown. We came to a car checker writing up a train in the yards, and Bert asked when there'd be a train leaving for the border town of Emerson. The checker told us there was one due at 2:20, and another at 9:30 at night. "But," he cautioned, "you better take the night train if you're thinking of crossing the border, because the Mounties work hand in glove with American Immigration on the other side. They cover the yards, and if they pick you up and don't hold you, they warn the Americans to be on the lookout for you. You better jump off the train before you get there and give Emerson and Noyes a wide berth."

After thanking the checker and leaving the yards, I asked, "How far is it uptown? I'm getting hungry."

"Yeah, I'm hungry too, but uptown's too far off. We have to save our legs for tonight. You heard what the checker said about bypassing Emerson and Noyes. That's going to take a hell of a lot of walking, so we need all the rest we can get. When we come to a store we'll get enough grub for today and tomorrow. Then we'll find a bank and trade our dough for American. We'll cook up something in the jungle."

There were four bos in the jungle when we got there. A loner was shaving while his clothes were coming to a boil in a five-gallon oil can. The other three were sitting on a log, dunking punk in the mulligan gravy of the stew they were eating from half-pound tobacco cans. The pungent odor of the mulligan simmering on the fire tightened my stomach.

"Man oh man, that mulligan smells good," I said.

I didn't know what I said to piss Bert off, but I knew he was mad when he snapped, "If you're that goddamn hungry, fan your ass into the bush and rustle up some firewood while I wash a pan to fry the ham and eggs in."

I was heading into the bush, when one of the bos on the log said, "There ain't no need to cook your ham and eggs. Tie into that mulligan. There's more'n we can eat, and it'll stick to your ribs better. We're fresh out of punk, but I reckon you got plenty yourself."

I would have enjoyed the mulligan more if I hadn't been worried about pissing Bert off. But after the three left and the loner was downstream rinsing his clothes, I asked Bert what I'd done.

"Forget it," he said. "I jumped on you quick because I didn't want us to get pegged for jungle buzzards. Paying compliments to jungle cooks is one of the ways buzzards begin the jungle. I intended to mention it later when we were alone. And now's a good time to point something else out, about the code or the law of the jungle. Call it what you like, but live by it when you're in the jungle. Did you notice before the three bums left they washed the coffee cans and other tins they used? Look where they are now, every one of them turned upside down to keep them dry inside when it rains. Good hobos and tramps treat the jungle like it was their home—and to some it is. That's why if you know the rules and live by them you won't get in any trouble. I thought the mulligan smelled good too, but I kept clammed up. I knew when they got their fill they'd tell us to dig in."

The pots and cans were taken care of and we were smoking when Bert said, "Now's a good time to get rid of everything that's got any sign of Canada on it. Go through your pack and cut the labels off your clothes, and don't forget the ones you're wearing. I'll roll enough smokes to last until we can buy more on the other side."

After removing all the labels, we moseyed up the tracks to the junction where the checker had told us we could catch the train to the border. A small jungle there had no occupants, and the improvised eating and cooking utensils scattered around were full of bullet holes.

Bert pointed at the mess and said, "Look at that mess. Some town clowns and railroad bulls get their nuts off wrecking the jungle and using the pots and cans for target practice. But when it's time for supper, we'll find enough tins and cans cached in the bush. Hobos always cache extra cans in the nearby bush."

CHAPTER 4

WE JUMPED OFF THE TRAIN JUST NORTH OF THE Emerson yard, left the railroad right-of-way, and spent a few minutes getting our bearings before taking to open fields around the border towns of Emerson and Noyes. Beyond Noyes we cut back to the Great Northern main line and knew by the railway signs that we had crossed the U.S. border. Then we walked the tracks to Humbolt, where we waited for a southbound train in a willow grove beside a stream.

We had it made, but were too frazzle-assed from the long night's walk to talk, and too hungry to sleep without eating. We ate fast, then flattened out on the dew-soaked grass and passed out.

The following day three trains balled the jack through town without stopping, and by nightfall we had no food left. When another train went roaring through we knew we'd had the course.

"Shit," said Bert, "we've thrown craps. Those redball trains don't have any reason to stop here, and it's too close to Noyes to have a meet with a northbound train. We got two choices: heel-and-toe it to Hallock through the night, or wait here for the way freight—and that could be two days."

Hungry but rested we walked the rails to Hallock, Minnesota. Day was breaking when we came to an abandoned livery stable on the outskirts of town and holed up in it until Hallock came to life. Then we mingled with the early risers and walked to the Town Café.

We'd just finished breakfast and were having a smoke with our coffee when two uniforms, one tall, one short and bald, walked in and asked the waitress if she'd called the sheriff. She nodded at us, but spoke too low for us to hear what she was saying. She was still flapping her lips when the tallest cop said, "Stop mumbling, girl, there's nothing to be afraid of. What makes you think they're Canadians?"

When she piped up we heard her loud and clear, and everybody else in the joint could too. "I didn't suspect them when they first came in," she said, "'cause Americans often come in here when they get off a morning freight. But I called the sheriff when I saw them eating with their forks upside down. Like Canadians do."

"Smart girl," said the tall one. "We'll take it from here now. Thanks."

Like treed raccoons we stayed put until the men came over. The tall one started firing questions but the other one interrupted. "We're going to need some answers, boys, but this isn't the place. Finish your coffee and come with us."

Outside, they took us to a sedan parked beside the curb. The tall one opened the rear door, and we got in. He slammed the door, then got behind the wheel with the short guy beside him and headed north for the border.

On the way there we learned that the tall one's name was Casey and his bald buddy answered to Maury. We had no inkling of what they planned and hoped the worst they'd do was send us back to Canada.

Everything came unraveled at American Immigration. We followed them into an office where one guy sat at a desk playing solitaire and one at another desk typing.

The typist looked up, nodded at Mutt and Jeff and went back to poking the keys with his index fingers. The other slapped down his cards and growled, "You guys picked a hell of a day to be late. You knew Pete and I were going fishing. We were supposed to meet Percy and Red a fuckin' hour ago—and we still have to get home, eat and change. Goddamn it, Case! You knew Pete and me been planning this outing for a month."

Casey raised his arms like he was surrendering. "I don't blame you for getting your hackles up, Keith, but there wasn't a damn thing Maury and I could do. If you want to blame somebody, blame the sheriff. He's the one made us late."

"What the hell's the sheriff got to do with you being late? And where did ya pick up these characters?" the man called Keith asked.

"He had plenty to do with it," said Maury. "But you're in a hurry. So why not read it in the report tonight? It's a pretty long story."

"To hell with that. A few minutes more ain't gonna make any difference now."

"Okay, but it's going to take longer than you think." And with a sly wink at Casey, Maury started in: "Mavis and I were almost finished breakfast when the phone rang. Neither one of us made a move to answer it. Finally Mavis said, 'Aren't you going to answer the phone? Nobody calls me this early in the morning. It might be important.' So I said, 'It's your phone. You answer it. I spend all day answering phones at the office.' So she left the table and answered the phone. 'It's for you, Maury,' she said. 'Who is it?' I said. 'I don't know, and I don't like to ask, because I think it's ignorant to ask people what their name is when it's not you they want to talk to,' she told me."

"For Christ's sake," yelled Keith. "Get to the point. You fuckin' well know we're in a hurry. That's why you're giving me all this bullshit. Tell me about the sheriff."

"Okay. But you said another minute wouldn't matter. Anyway it was the sheriff on the phone, and he told me the waitress at the Town Café had called to tell him two Canadians were eating breakfast there. He asked if Casey and I would check it out and save him a trip to the border."

Keith got to his feet. "Okay, smartass, you've had your fun. But it'll cost you a feed of fresh trout. Let's get the hell out of here, Pete. Case can finish that fuckin' report. If we fan our asses we'll still have time to get a coupla fish before dark." He stormed out the door and Pete followed.

Maury herded Bert and me into a small room and left us to stew. So I stewed. I was spouting more sweat than a Finn in a sauna when I asked Bert what we'd tell the Immigration guys when they asked us where we were from.

"I'll tell them I'm from Spokane," Bert answered. "I holed up there for six weeks last year—waiting for the Montana lambing season. I bet all they know about Spokane is that it's logging country in the state of Washington. You're the one I'm worried about. They'll question us separately, so for Christ's sake don't tell them we're buddies. Tell them you're from Redding. That's a division town on the Northern Pacific Railroad in northern California. They're going to ask you about me, and when they do, tell them you don't know me from a windrow of assholes. We met in the jungle at Minot and teamed up because we were both going to Chicago. I'll say the same thing."

They split us up. Maury put me in a room and left me alone for twenty minutes. And every minute I sat there, the knot in my gut got tighter. When he finally came to question me, I was scared fartless but glad to get it over with. When he asked me where my home was and I told him Redding, California, he put his hand in his pocket, smiled knowingly and said, "Calgary's a lot farther north than that, son. And that's where you're from." It was like getting smacked in the kisser with a fresh fish. How the hell did he know that? Bert was the only one who knew that, and I couldn't believe he'd ratted on me.

Maury saw the amazed look on my kisser, grinned and pulled something out of his pocket. "You're wondering how I know about Calgary," he said. "I know a hell of a lot more than that. I know you're a pretty good hockey player. Have a look at this. You did a pretty good job of getting rid of your identity, but I found this in the watch pocket of the jeans in your pack. You cut the logo off the jeans, but you forgot to check the watch pocket. What's the inscription on it read?" And he handed me a bronze medal the size of a silver dollar.

He had me cold. I knew it by heart. Under my name it said:

Calgary Beavers
City Midget Hockey
1921
Champions

I pocketed the medal and said, "Now that you know I'm Canadian, give me back my pack and I'll go home."

"I wish for the both of us it was as easy as that, but it's not, and there's not a goddamn thing I can do about it. Canada won't take you back without proof that you're a Canadian citizen, and we have

to hold you until you get your birth certificate or other proof."
Three things flashed through my mind when Maury told me this:
How could I have thought Bert would rat on me? How would I be
able to cope with being held for deportation alone? How would I be
able to convince Maury that I only met Bert in Minot and took the
same train to Chicago he did? But Maury surprised me again when
he said, "You're going to have company while you're waiting for
your ID. Your buddy Bert wasn't any more thorough than you
were. Casey found a letter in your buddy's packsack from his sister
in Manitoba. You'll both be held in the Hallock County Jail until
you can clear the border. Then we'll ship you back to Winnipeg."

CHAPTER 5

THE SANDSTONE JAIL, THE THREE-STORY BELL-towered courthouse and the sheriff's quarters sat in a block-square courtyard. The blond rangey Swede sheriff was a tolerant man in his early forties whose aloofness in dealing with inmates was appreciated by most prisoners, for they had no desire to become bosom pals with lawmen. Still, his judgements when controversial issues arose, although stern, were honest and not without compassion.

In the main the prisoners were illegal immigrants being held for deportation, plus a few first-time losers, all ignorant of kangaroo courts. But the inmates had an unelected arbiter whose judgement was accepted without question any time a dispute needed settling. He was Dave McFadden, a stocky articulate Scot in his late thirties. When he spoke, the smile on his weatherworn kisser convinced everyone he was honest and won him the respect of both the prisoners and the sheriff.

McFadden had migrated to Canada four years before. For two years he worked as a farm laborer in summer and logged in the winter. Then he filed on a homestead in northern Ontario. He spent his summers working on the homestead to meet government proving-up requirements and his winters in Wisconsin's logging camps where wages were higher than Ontario bush-camp pay. He needed every penny he could scrape together.

The previous summer, Dave's oldest sister had met and married a Scottish policeman from Winnipeg and was now living there. After spring break-up, on his return to the homestead, Dave detoured through Winnipeg to visit his sister, and was nabbed at the border. Dave and his redheaded cell mate, Bryn Brighton, a huge and boisterous twenty-seven-year-old Australian, and the biggest man in the jail, had a common bond: they were not Canadians. It had been weeks since they wrote home for their birth certificates. When their proof of citizenship came, they would be shipped to their homelands, not Canada. So they planned to escape and flee back across the border.

Bert and I had been given a four-bunk cell to ourselves, but on our fourth night there the sheriff put a violent young Norwegian in with us. It had taken the sheriff and a posse two days to track down and capture him in a swamp after he'd gone berserk and nearly killed his ex-girlfriend and her new suitor.

We had followed the account of the sheriff's hunt for the deranged suitor in the paper that was delivered daily to the jail. So when the sheriff was leaving, Bert followed him into the corridor and asked why he hadn't put the prisoner in the padded cell.

"I considered it," the sheriff said. "But he comes from a well-respected family and has never been in trouble before. He's passive now and shouldn't give you any trouble. It's only for tonight. He'll be going to the mental hospital to be assessed in the morning. Incidentally, as you must know from reading the papers, his name is Olaf Peterson. But it might ease the situation if you and your buddy introduced yourselves and asked him his name."

When Bert got back to our cell, Olaf, who'd been roaming the swamp for two days and nights, was asleep on my lower bunk, so we never introduced ourselves. We were the last inmates to hit the pad, and Bert took the precaution of abandoning his lower for the other upper. I'd be lying if I said we slept well. Although we should have, because Olaf was still sleeping when the attendants from the mental hospital came to get him in the morning.

After Olaf had been taken away and normalcy restored, the sheriff allowed the prisoners the run of the jail. The only off-limits areas were the upstairs corridors between the cell block and the wall of barred windows, the admitting area and two small rooms adjoining the large exercise room downstairs that was left open around the clock.

The saltpeter-laced unpalatable jail food was catered by the Town Café. It was served in mess kits and passed in through a seven-inch-square opening in the bars between the admitting room and the stairway to the second-floor cell block. Knowing the quality of food was poor, the sheriff permitted a local store to take orders and deliver magazines, stationery, razor blades, soap, tobacco and cigarettes.

Except for loss of liberty, confinement did little to alter the mode of recreation of the working stiffs. Aside from the rare trips to towns to blow their stakes on bootleg moonshine and whores (for they had no qualms about breaking Prohibition or moral laws), they did the same things in jail as in the jungles and isolated work camps. The gamblers still shot craps and played poker or blackjack. The literate still read the daily newspapers, current journals and magazines. And the talkers still carried on their long-winded bull sessions.

Although I sat in on the bull sessions I kept my clapper idle, because the first thing I learned—and I learned much at those bull sessions—was not to wag your tongue if you had nothing of interest to say. Sitting there quietly and listening was like attending college with hobo professors. It would have taken years of hardship roughing it on the road for me to learn the road lore I soaked up at those sessions.

Also, almost daily we had at least one diversion from the jail routine. One caper everyone got a bang out of was when the sheriff or deputy brought a prisoner in to the lockup. They would intentionally bring him to the partition between the admitting area and the jail, rattle the big key ring on the bars, and holler, "Fresh meat!" On cue we'd rush to the partition, screaming and hollering obscenities, while we clawed through the bars.

"Ain't that a dainty ass?"

"You're goddamn right. He can warm my bunk."

"Like hell he will. This one's mine."

"Screw you. I saw him first."

"I don't give a damn who else has him—but after I'm finished."

To prolong the prisoner's anxiety, the sheriff or deputy would fumble with the keys, trying every key on the ring but the right one, to keep the poor guy sweating it out. The blow-off came when the door was slammed shut on the terrified bastard's ass. Then everyone suddenly turned their backs and left him alone by the door.

But the big caper was on a night the sheriff and deputy brought in a moonshiner. After we'd scared the crap out of him with our usual screaming routine, Dave took him upstairs to assign him a bunk while Bryn and I watched the sheriff and deputy lug the evidence into the admitting area. I was turning to leave, when Bryn grabbed my arm.

"Hold it. Let's wait until the sheriff and deputy lock up."

Usually the sheriff put the evidence in one of the small lockup rooms, but Bryn must have had a premonition. That night, maybe because it was after nine and he was bushed, the sheriff just left everything on the admitting-room floor, ten feet from the partition. When he and the deputy had gone I looked at Bryn, noted the grin on his kisser and asked, "What the hell you so happy about? What did you see?"

"It's not what I saw. It's what I'm thinking. But I have to talk to the moonshiner and find out if those two big jugs are filled with what I think they are. Come on!" He wheeled and took the stairs two at a time with me following.

Dave was playing solitaire in his cell. Bryn asked him where he'd put the moonshiner. "In the cell at the east end of the other bank of cells," he said. "But I don't think he's in the mood for visitors. What's your interest, anyway? You've never wanted to be on a welcoming committee before."

"Then you go ask what's in those demijohns the sheriff left in admitting. If they're full of moonshine, there's enough liquor in them to keep every man in the can piss limber-drunk for a week," Bryn said.

Dave laughed. "Lets go ask him. His name's Sven."

Bryn raced ahead, and before we reached the other bank of cells Dave yelled, "Hold up, Bryn. What the hell's the rush? Don't you know the older whisky gets the better it is? It's better you wait here while I go find out."

Dave liked to ham it up. When he came out of Sven's cell he kicked up his heels like a four-month filly turned out to pasture. Then, adding flourish to his act, he pranced up the aisle like a stud horse approaching a mare at a snorting pole.

"Look at the goofy bastard," Bryn grinned. "From the act he's putting on I'd say we're in. He's mind-guzzling and half pissed already."

When Dave's gymnastics ended, he whispered: "Sven says those jugs are filled to the stoppers with the best wheat whisky this side of the border."

When we got downstairs and Dave saw the demijohns he exploded. "Christ almighty, man! I don't know why you were so bloody anxious to find out what was in those jugs. It doesn't matter if it's liquor or horse piss. They're ten feet from the goddamn partition, and there ain't a man in here with arms that long."

Bryn laughed. "So what's the matter with putting an extension on somebody's arm? Ain't you ever heard of that? And the sheriff was kind enough to leave us the material to do it with. Take the laces out of those logging boots you're wearing and give them to me. If I can't get those jugs over here, I'll drop my strides and let every man in the can boot my ass."

"Don't tell me you're good enough with a lasso to rope those jugs from here?"

"Hell no. I'm going to snag that coil of copper condenser tubing and drag it over. And I need one of your boots, too. Dave knelt and slowly unlaced his boots. "For Christ's sake," hissed Bryn. "Hurry up."

"Why the hell don't you use your own boots if you're in such a rush?"

"One, you've got the biggest feet in the joint. Two, you're the only man in here wearing fourteen-inch logging boots. And I need a heavy boot as well as long laces. So don't give me a hard time."

When the boot was tied to the laces Bryn pushed it through the bars. After three tosses it landed in the center of the coil, and Bryn gingerly dragged it across the floor to the bars. "So what did I tell ya?" he smirked. "But I don't know whether to credit Australia for brains or Scotland for big feet."

Dave scowled, then shot back, "You're bright, bo, I give you that. But the only reason is because you were probably christened with the piss of a Scotsman."

By then Bryn had got hold of the coil. But since it was too big to get through the bars, he straightened it out and pulled it through.

Then he snapped off a section, shaped it into a shepherd's crook, snagged the nearest jug and dragged it over to the barred partition.

"We should say a prayer of thanks to the Scotsman that supplied the piss," said Dave, "because thanks to him and Bryn's engineering genius we'll drink tonight."

Surprisingly, Bryn ignored the needle once again, but I don't think he was listening. When he finally got his hands on the jug, he rocked it back and forth to wet the cork, before pulling the cork out and sticking it on his tongue. "Holy Jesus, Dave! Sven sure as hell knows what he's talking about when he says this is good stuff."

To get into the act, I took a clean handkerchief out of my pocket, rolled it lengthwise and stuck it in the neck of the jug until it got soaked. Then I handed it to Dave. He took it, opened his mouth, squeezed the liquor into it and swallowed. Tears oozed from his eyes, and when he stopped gasping for breath he said, "Christ almighty! That little Scandinavian never said it was pure alky. It must be over a hundred- sixty proof."

"That," Bryn snickered, "evened the score. Sven don't know it, but he just squared things between you and me for that crack of yours about my christening."

Then he picked up the coil, snapped a piece off the end and took it with him when we went upstairs to get something to put the liquor in.

Over the years other prisoners had bought a hot plate, a two-gallon coffee pot, and twenty or thirty enamelware mugs, which were kept in an empty cell. When we got there Josh was in the cell taking mugs off the divider of an upturned orange crate. Coffee was brewing on the hot plate on top of the orange crate.

At forty-eight, Josh was the oldest man in the jail. He was a snaggle-toothed gnome whose life on the road and careless health habits had aged him beyond his years. Like many small men he had the cockiness of a bantam rooster, and he never tired of saying, "I may be small, but I never did, and never will, take shit off any man if I'm right and he's wrong." (Although Josh was seldom right.) "I don't give a good goddamn how big the guy is."

None of us took Josh seriously. Bryn, especially, loved to rib him just to see the little character explode. In spite of that, Josh liked Bryn—because Bryn had bailed him out of a couple of scrapes his mouth got him into. So when we entered the cell, Bryn slapped him on the back and said, "I'm sorry you went to the trouble of making coffee, Josh. You should have checked with me first, because I've decided there's not going to be any coffee drinking in the jail tonight, so dump the coffee in the crapper. I need the pot."

Josh swung around as bristly as a bitch with a litter of pups. "Who the fuck gave you the right to tell me or anyone else they can't have a cup of coffee if they want one?"

Bryn smiled. "I know you're tough, Josh. But I mean what I say. And all your hollering and swearing won't make a goddamn bit of difference, because I don't scare easy. How the hell you figure to get out of here with that pot? There's three of us and one of you."

"I'll tell you how," Josh snarled, grabbing the handle of the pot. "Come any closer and see what happens. I don't give a damn if you are my friends, I'll scald the fucking nuts off you."

Bryn raised a hand. "Okay, Josh, you gutsy little bastard, if that's the way you want it, you win. But sometimes to win is to lose. And if you don't dump the coffee, you'll lose. Wouldn't you rather strut around the jail dishing out mugs of whisky instead of coffee? Because if you dump that swamp piss like I told you, I'll fill that pot with the best alky you ever drank."

"You big son of a bitch," Josh beamed. "Why in hell didn't you say that in the first place?"

"Because I get a bang outta seeing your pressure build up. You let off more steam than a road hog blowing down. A guy'd go nuts in here if he couldn't get a laugh now and then."

"You bastard," Josh said, then laughed. He dumped the coffee pot and watched Dave opening the crimped end of the tubing with the point of a can opener. He then put a hundred-and-eighty-degree curve in one end of the tubing before we all trooped back downstairs to the jug.

Bryn reached through the bars, pulled the stopper, shoved the straight end of the tubing in the jug and said, "I'll hold the pot. But since you're the senior man in the can, Josh, you get the honor of starting the siphon. But watch it. We've tried it. It'll slap you on your ass faster than running into a clothesline in the dark."

We had another laugh at Josh when he sucked the hooch to the end of the tube and gulped enough to flatten a mule. If he'd been whacked on the head with a twelve-pound spike maul it wouldn't have knocked him on his ass any faster. He couldn't breathe, and his face got redder than a wobbly flag. The moonshine gushing from the tube to the floor didn't faze him. Let it spill. Only survival mattered.

Bryn shoved the pot beneath the gusher before too much spilled, while Dave cured Josh's spasm by smacking his back until Josh gasped, "Christ, hold it, Dave. The fucking cure's worse than the bite. Sorry, Bryn, but it's bin so long since I had a drink, I couldn't resist taking a swallow."

When the pot and six mugs I had taken downstairs were filled we went upstairs to share the spoils. And knowing Josh would put on a show if we let him serve the first round to the poker players, we followed.

But so many kibitzers were watching the game Josh had to squeeze his way into the cell with the mugs held over his head. "About time you got here," one player griped. "You been gone long enough to grow the fucking beans."

"If you want to blame somebody," said Josh, "blame Dave and Bryn, not me. They took the pot to soak their socks in, and wouldn't give it back. Said to give you a drink of this, you'd like it better'n coffee." Then he lowered the three mugs to Art Jenkins's nose.

"What the fuck is this?" growled Art. Then he got a whiff of the alky, and the scowl became a smile a block wide. "Where the hell'd you get it? You weren't shooting the shit when you said it beat coffee." He tossed his cards aside, stood up and said, "Deal me out. I'm going to go find out if there's more where this stuff came from."

"Ain't no need to do that," said Josh, "'cuz there's aplenty. Enough to make every man in here loop-legged drunk for three days. But I'm warning you; don't drink it uncut or you ain't gonna breathe again till you reach the pearly gates." He put the six mugs of alky on the table, and six hands scooped them up.

Then Art came charging out of the cell and saw us. "I don't know how you characters managed to get a hold of this stuff," he said with a grin, "but if you're passing it around, I'd sure as hell like a share."

"You got no worries on that score, Art," said Dave. "There's enough for everybody. Round up the rest of the guys and go to the space in front of the stairs. We'll get the mugs and bring them there. It's the only place big enough for everyone—and the water's just around the corner."

Everyone in the jail except Sven, who declined, was sitting in a circle on the floor, passing the six water-cut mugs of alky from one to the other when we arrived with the giggle water. They started clapping, and one guy shouted, "Let's give three cheers for the three whisketeers." But Dave raised his hand and said, "Hold it! Can the noise. We, along with Sven, accept the thanks, because I know every man here enjoys a drink of liquor as much as I do, and I'd suck it out of a kangaroo's pouch if he was running forty miles an hour uphill. But we're not in a bootleg joint where we can cut loose. So we have to keep the noise down. Get as drunk as you like—but do it quietly. Because the first son of a bitch that starts raising hell is going to get knocked colder than a dead whore's tits in a snowbank." Then he put a hand on my shoulder. "Now our buddy here is too young to do any drinking, so he'll do the bartending. And if anyone starts to get loud, he's going to cut them off."

I took the coffee pot from Bryn. While I was pouring shots into the mugs and the men were cutting them with water to suit their tastes, Art Jenkins stood up and said, "You heard what Dave said and I'm backing him all the way, but that doesn't mean we can't pay these guys a tribute. So when everybody gets a drink, let's stand up and drink a toast to them."

When everybody had a drink they stood up and raised their mugs to us. This kicked off a series of obscene toasts that lasted half an hour, until one of the guys started getting pissed and would rather be heard than listen.

Art Jenkins asked for quiet, and when things died down, he gave me the handle I've answered to ever since. I'm not a moniker bum like "The Mover" and others like him who've carved their nom de plume on every railroad station's shithouse wall from coast to coast. But I'm known in many jungles by the handle Art hung on me that night in the Hallock County Jail.

A former wobbly organizer experienced in handling drunken hecklers at sidewalk meetings, Art waved his arms like Jesus on the mount, and said, "Shut up, everyone! I've got something important to say." He looked at me. "For a young guy that's all legs and hasn't been around much, you handle yourself pretty good, yuh sonofabitch. But as a bartender you're the shits. You got to know when a man's getting pissed and water down his drinks before he gets out of hand. This bash is getting so loud it won't be long till the sheriff'll be charging in here to find out what the racket's all about." He went on to suggest with authority that the celebrants break up into small groups, so guys could talk together quietly without needing to shout over the interruptions. Then he finished up by saying, "But before we go, I'd like to give a toast to our leggy bartender." And, raising his mug, he said:

"Here's to a young man called Legs
When he's broke and he's hungry, he begs.
He can't settle down, because he must roam,
So an empty boxcar and the jungle's his home.
He works on farms and he works in camps,
And beats his way with hobos and tramps.
Without him or the rest of his kind,
The country would be caught in a bind.
So drink to him, men, he's the salt of the earth.
He's midwifed the land and toiled there since birth."

The men all mumbled remarks of assent and drank the toast. Then, when Dave assured them that Legs would still look after their drinking needs, including the water chaser, they went to different cells with their cronies and the noise died down.

Bert and three guys about my age from Winnipeg went to one cell. They were drinking very little and I spent my time with them— when I wasn't pouring drinks—until they called it a night.

When the clock in the courthouse chimed midnight, the only men still awake were six poker players and two kibitzers in one cell and Dave, Bryn and me in another listening to Art telling stories about police, scabs, saboteurs, Pinkerton provocateurs and stool pigeons during his wobbly days.

By three in the morning the drinking had tapered off and Dave told me to hit the sack, but I said I'd rather stay up and listen to Art's stories. About daybreak I went to the can and was flushing it when I got an idea. Excited by the thought I rushed back to the cell. "There's a crapper no one uses in the padded cell," I said. "Why don't we fix it so it won't flush, and fill the tank with moonshine? There's a chance the sheriff won't find it when he searches." It broke up the gabfest.

To reach the tank on the wall near the ceiling, Bryn stood on the bunk to unhook the float from the lever that lifts it. Then he took the pot of alky from Dave, emptied it in the tank and said, "It'll hold more. Why not fill it?" So I went downstairs, got another potfull and brought it to Bryn who dumped in another half pot of alky. Then we left three mugs half filled with pure alky on the floor to account for the alky odor in the cell.

More than half the inmates missed breakfast. I would have, too, if Bert hadn't wakened me in time to wash and get in line.

The deputy spotted the moonshine jug against the partition when he unlocked the door for the caterers and high-tailed it for the sheriff before the first mess kit passed through the partition opening.

I was at the head of the chow line when the sheriff came blasting through the door. He went to the jug, grabbed it by the lug, hefted it and asked, "Where's McFadden?"

"I haven't seen him this morning. Maybe he's still in bed," I stammered.

"He won't be sleeping very long," the sheriff snarled. He unlocked the partition door, walked in with the deputy then relocked it before heading upstairs to find Dave.

Thirty seconds after the deputy bolted for the sheriff, Dave had word by the grapevine. And so, dressed, washed, shaved and neatly groomed, Dave beat the sheriff to the head of the stairs. "Good morning, sheriff." He smiled. "You're early today."

"McFadden, you got more brass than the Liberty Bell, and they had to cast it three times. Don't 'Good morning' me, you sonofabitch. You and every fucking man in here are gonna find out that that pissup last night was the costliest binge you ever had. The whole goddamn gang of you are in serious trouble if I lay charges for destroying state evidence."

Dave nodded. "I know you have a good reason for being pissed off with what happened, but look at it from this side of the bars. There's pro and con for everything. Last night a situation arose, and some men took advantage of it. For them it was a big deal and broke the monotony of being cooped up. There wasn't any rowdiness, nothing got smashed up. The men enjoyed themselves with the state as their host—yet at no cost to it. Beside, you still have lots of evidence. And when the trial's over you're going to pour it down the sewer. If you enjoy a drink—and I've never met a Swede that didn't—try and put yourself in the men's place when you're handing out punishment."

You could see the sheriff's anger melting as Dave talked. When he finished the sheriff shook his head. "McFadden you missed your calling. You should have taken up law. You've goddamn near got me believing nothing out of the way happened here last night. But I've still gotta lean on everyone here. You can't run a jail without discipline. If I did what's expected of me, I'd lay charges for destroying state's evidence. Since there's enough left for a conviction, I'll drop the charges. But everyone in jail's gonna lose the freedom they've had till now. After I've searched the jail, I'm racking everyone in their cell. And I'm keeping them there till I figure it's time to become lax again. You'll be allowed out of your cells three times a day—to wash, to use the toilets and for meals. Now I want every man to go to the exercise room and stay there until we finish searching."

The sheriff and deputy combed the jail for an hour and found only the half-filled coffee pot and partly filled mugs of cut liquor. From the exercise room we could hear the toilets flushing, so we took it for granted that my idea of hiding the moonshine was as worthless as a gun without a trigger.

Two days later the sheriff relented. He gave us a blast that was more of a warning than a threat, then left the jail without locking us in our cells. Art beat me to the padded cell and was standing on the bunk sniffing the hand he'd drawn from the flush tank. "What the hell d'ya know?" he yelped. "The booze's still here. We best go tell Dave and Bryn, and see what they want to do with it."

"Far as I'm concerned, I'm for doing like the Limeys do aboard ship, and give everyone a daily ration for as long as it lasts," Dave said.

We all agreed and appointed Art booze master.

CHAPTER 6

BERT AND I EACH GOT LETTERS TWO WEEKS AFTER
the booze caper. Bert's mother's letter had his birth certificate
enclosed, and he would be shipped back to Canada when the
bureaucrats got their paperwork done. My stepfather's letter told
me he had sent to Quebec for my birth certificate. When I read it I
got worried, because compulsory birth registration laws were not in
force when I was born, and I didn't know whether either my
parents or the hospital had registered my arrival. It turned out
later I had reason to worry.

Four European inmates in the jail had neglected to apply for
Canadian citizenship papers and were no nearer the door than they
were when nabbed at the border six months before. When proof of
their citizenship came they'd be shipped back home, and I pictured
myself sharing the jail's diet of salt-petered horse cock with them
until I got proof of birth.

Bert tried to put my mind at ease by telling me a birth certificate
was not the only thing that would prove I was Canadian. But this
was little comfort, for I knew that any ID would be hard to come by.
When I was young and my father was alive, we had no permanent
mooring. He was a dirt contractor who built roadbeds for Canada's
railroads, which, like Canada, were growing fast. To keep abreast
of the growth, my father moved his family from job site to job site.

I lay on my bunk trying to forget my worries and sleep. Everyone,
I thought, had been asleep in the soundless jail for an hour. Then
I heard muffled footsteps shuffling down the corridor. Looking up,
I saw Dave and Bryn sock-footing it past my cell. Curiosity took my
mind off my worries but became a further deterrent to sleep.
Twenty minutes later I got off my bunk, pulled on my socks and
strides and crept downstairs to see what they were up to. At the
bottom of the stairs I heard sounds like a wooden match scratching
on a cement wall. The noise came from the corner of the exercise
room where the outside wall joined the wall with the door. Cautiously
I stopped at the door and looked inside.

Dave and Bryn had pulled the corner radiator onto the floor and were kneeling on it, scraping and pecking like woodpeckers at the mortar in the brick wall behind it. I figured this wasn't the first night they'd been working on the wall, because a brick lay on the rad.

I watched from the doorway until they pulled another brick from the wall and grinned at each other before shoving it back in. While they were standing the rad back up I slipped upstairs to my bunk— knowing they were opening the gate to Canada for me.

In my excitement I was tempted to wake Bert and tell him my hopes, but then thought better of it and tried to sleep. What a night! First worry had kept me awake. Then curiosity. And finally, sheer excitement. Instead of sleeping I was high-tailing it to Canada in the light of a full moon. As the sun rose I was belting across the border, until sleep finally slugged me out. I awoke in panic, struggling to free myself from an immigration officer. The dream was so realistic that when I opened my eyes and saw Bert shaking me awake for the chow line, I hopped out of bed flailing my arms and would have flopped on my ass if he hadn't grabbed me.

"What the hell were you dreaming about? When I called you for chow, you pulled the blanket over your head and started mumbling. And when I yanked the blanket off and started shaking you, you jumped me like a punchdrunk fighter."

"I thought I was crossing the border," I mumbled. "And when you started shaking me I thought you were an immigration officer. I guess that's why I came up slugging. I couldn't sleep last night, and I'm glad. After we eat there's something I have to tell you. I think I've got my ticket outta here."

Bert didn't press for more, and after breakfast I told him what I'd seen and that I intended to take it on the lam, too.

"Have you asked Bryn and Dave if they'll take you with them?" Bert asked.

"No. And I don't think I will. I'll wait until they're gone, then go myself. They may not want to take me. And I wouldn't want them to think because I saw them working on the wall I might rat on them if they said no."

Knowing Bert, I should have known when he walked away without a word that he'd do what he thought best for me. And I shouldn't have been surprised when he told me an hour later he'd talked to Dave and Bryn and they had agreed to take me.

"Fantastic!" I said. "But how did you put it to them?"

"I told them we've known for two days they were getting ready to go through the wall, and you were going to lam out of here by yourself after they'd gone."

"Christ, Bert! If I live to be a hundred I'll never be able to thank you enough. Did you have any trouble getting them to take me along?"

"Hell, no. They like you, and they know the trouble you're having getting proof of citizenship. But now they're worried. They figure it'll take four or five more nights before they'll have enough bricks out of the wall to crash their way out. And they're afraid a wrong guy might wander downstairs, see what they're doing and tell the sheriff."

Hoping I could speed up the job, I went to Dave and offered to lend a hand. "We know you'd like to help," he said, "but there's only room for two men to work at the same time and we've got the knack now. The day after tomorrow, start ordering some stuff from the store to eat on the way to the border. We'll need enough for two days, because this time of year the nights are short and we can only travel after dark."

For the next two nights, while Bryn and Dave worked on the wall, I lay on my bunk sweating it out—my peepers open and my ears alert till they came back upstairs to their bunks. Then I'd go to sleep and pound my ear until Bert roused me for chow. Two mornings later, right after chow, the sheriff and deputy gave every cell and corridor a thorough check before summoning everyone to the exercise room. We sweated it out. I was certain some wisenheimer had learned about our intended break and ratted.

But the sheriff simply said: "I know you get the local weekly paper and the Minneapolis daily, so you know this is the opening day of the County Court Assizes. None of you are under indictment, so the Grand Jury means nothing to you. Still, it's the jury's duty to inspect the jail, and they'll question some prisoners. But watch what you tell them. If you have any gripes, bring them to me. I'll straighten them out a lot quicker and easier on my own without a lot of bullshit from the jury. Most of the cells are neat and clean, but there's a few that aren't and I want them shipshape. I want four men to come with me to get brooms, mops, soap and pails. We're gonna unlock the corridor doors so you can sweep and mop them as well as the cells. If I can't get volunteers I'll appoint them."

During the tour of the jail, the Grand Jury questioned a few prisoners, but left by ten o'clock. Josh immediately started aping the tall, skinny jury member with the squeaky voice who'd asked the most questions. Bryn, who loved riling Josh, winked at me and cracked, "You surprise me acting like that, Josh. You know perfectly well that guy and the rest of the Grand Jury have our best interests at heart. I'll bet they spend half their lives sticking up for the rights of us poor unfortunates. By coming here today they may have made it possible for some of us to get out of here before sunset."

"Bullshit!" Josh snorted. "Now I know why you goddamn Aussies are still tied to England's apron strings. You can't think for yourselves. The Limeys'll be telling you forever what to do if everybody in Australia thinks like that."

During the laughter, Bryn slapped Josh's shoulder. "You're too quick to take the needle, man. You should know by now how I like to see you blow your cork. I think the same about vested authority, but I resent your crack about my countrymen. Let's fight."

Even Josh laughed at that. When he left to make a pot of coffee, Dave whispered, "Were you serious about some of us being out of here by sundown?"

"You're damn right I was." Bryn grinned. "I've been looking at the key for weeks. Come upstairs and I'll show it to you."

It had been seven years since two Stillwater Prison escapees were nabbed at the Canadian border and taken to Hallock until an escort from Stillwater came to get them. But a hacksaw blade hidden on one of them went undetected when they were searched, and they sawed their way to freedom again. And the repairman had welded the severed section of the bar instead of replacing it.

When we reached the top of the stairs, Bryn pointed at the cast-iron newel post at the top of the railing. On it sat a huge ornamental ball. "That post is hollow," Bryn said, "and the ball"—he tapped it with his knuckles— "is solid iron. And that's our key. I've been looking at it ever since I got locked up, but today's the first time I've had a chance to use it, because the corridor's always been locked." Then he gripped the ball with both hands and tried to unscrew it. When it didn't budge, he turned to Dave. "You take a crack at it," he said. "You're the arm-wrestling champ of the jail. If you can't unscrew it we're fucked. And it's back to working on the wall."

Dave clamped his fingers around the ball and strained till his neck muscles swelled. But after thirty seconds he let go with a gasp. "Like you said, Bryn, I guess we're fucked."

"Maybe it's the paint that's keeping it from turning," I said. "When you paint a window, sometimes you can't open it until you scrape the paint outta the cracks."

Dave pulled the sharpened spoon he'd been using on the wall from his denim jacket and said, "We'll soon know." He went to work on the joint of the ball and the newel post. After five minutes the paint was chiseled out—and the ball spun like a weathercock. He handed it to Bryn and grinned. "The ball's in your court now."

Bryn hefted it and said, "Christ, it must weigh at least twelve pounds! We're halfway home, but we still have a few hills to climb. Let's not do anything more until after chow when the runner gets here with the bread we ordered." And he screwed the ball back on the newel post.

But on that particular day, the chow was late. The county court sittings, like a country fair, drew the farmers to town like shad flies to light bulbs, and the Town Café was too busy feeding the scissor bills to serve the prisoners on time.

While waiting for the chow, we went to an upstairs window to case the grounds behind the jail. The county had already laid in the winter's supply of cordwood for the jail and courthouse boilers. The wood was piled ten feet high behind the jail in rows running halfway to the courthouse.

"They must of had us in mind," Dave said, "when they piled that cordwood there. When we hit the ground, if we duck between the rows we won't look as suspicious walking out from behind the courthouse as we would from the jail yard."

Bryn, who was anxious to get going, started cursing the Town Café. "Oh, for Christ's sake, Bryn," Bert said. "Calm down. You're as skittish as a mare with a rein beneath her tail. It doesn't matter to me, because I'm not going anywhere. But wouldn't it be better to stay here until it's dark?"

"Sure it would," said Bryn. "Anybody with one eye and an asshole could figure that out. But how do we know the doors will be open then? Every minute we sit here waiting increases the chance of the sheriff or deputy coming back and locking the door. I'm for giving the goddamn runner another fifteen minutes. If he's not here by then, we take off and make the border on an empty gut. It's ten to two already, and there's no way of knowing if he's even coming. What do you and Legs say, Dave?"

"I'm for it," Dave said. "The sooner we get out of here the better. What's your thinking, Legs? You willing to starve till we hit the border?"

"Me," I said, "I'm just a passenger. I'm ready to leave when the train pulls out. All I'm waiting for is the highball."

Bryn smiled. "Then it's settled. If the chuck's not here in fifteen minutes, we'll start bashing our way out and go hungry to the border."

The chow and the bread for our lump arrived at two. We bolted it down. Then, carrying the ball and four blankets, we went to the window with the welded bar. Bryn sliced an eighteen-inch strip off a blanket and folded it lengthwise. I held one end as he twisted it into a rope. Then I held the ball while he tied the rope in the groove between the mounting flange and the ball. Meanwhile, Dave tied the other three blankets together with square knots and fastened one to a bar of the cell across the corridor. Our ladder ready for descent, Bryn handed the makeshift maul to Dave, saying, "It's your honor, Dave. An old axman like you shouldn't have trouble using this."

Dave took the maul, stepped back from the window and took

three practice swings. Then he stepped up to the bar, wound up and belted the bar a Herculean blow that made the wall tremble. But the weld held. Undaunted, he swung again. On the fifth swing he hit pay dirt. The weld broke.

The blows had loosened the grout around the stub of the bar. Bryn pulled it out and tossed the loose end of the blankets out the enlarged opening in the bars. "Follow me, Legs, but wait till I hit the ground. The blankets might not be strong enough to hold us both at the same time."

I was out the window hanging on the bars by the time Bryn's feet hit the ground. When they did, I grabbed the blanket, shinned down it like a monkey on a vine and followed Bryn into the rows of stacked cordwood. Then Dave came charging toward us between the rows, and Bryn laughed loudly. "Look at that Scotchman run!" His unbuttoned jacket flapped in the breeze, and his bulging shirt with the punk stuffed inside it made him look like a pregnant woman in an obstacle course. His pockets, like mine and Bryn's, were crammed with rations for the hike. So we stayed in the woodpile till we emptied them into the paper bags I'd tucked in my shirt for that purpose.

We started out together, but then Dave stopped. "Hold it. Somebody might see us coming out and get suspicious. Let me go out first buttoning my fly as if I'd been in here having a piss. When I've taken a few steps I'll stop and finish buttoning up like I'm waiting for something. Then you two come out together as if you stayed in the woodpile to button up."

We nodded in agreement. Then he added, "We'll stop at the corner of the courthouse and gab a few seconds, then stroll out to the sidewalk. And listen, Legs, it's important for you to speak up if anyone asks us questions. If Bryn or I answer, our accents could land us back in the jug."

I nearly shit when we rounded the corner of the courthouse. The hayseeds were rushing out like pigs to a feed trough. Dave never gave it a second thought. "Court's recessed," he said. "That's a break I never expected. With all these people on the streets, it'll be harder for some nosy bastard to peg us as strangers."

We got a break before we got to the sidewalk. A group of straw-hatted scissor bills stopped on the pillared portico and blocked the exit while they argued the pros and cons of the case on trial. This stopped the traffic coming out and gave us enough walking room in the gap where we could talk quietly without being overheard.

Though it didn't seem logical to me, I hadn't questioned Bryn or Dave earlier in jail when they agreed to head for the jungle as soon as we hit the street. But now we were outside, I said, "Why are we going to the jungle? Isn't it the first place the sheriff'll look when he finds out we're gone?"

"You're right," said Dave. "It is. But if Bert pulled the blankets out of the window like he said he would, it might be quite a while before the sheriff finds out. The reason we feel it's better to go to the jungle first is because the natives are used to seeing bos and working stiffs heading there and it won't look as suspicious. But if we take to the fields or roads it will. I holed up there before I got picked up. There's a creek running through it with bush on both sides, and it parallels the track. We can stay out of sight in the bush till we're two or three miles out of town. Then we'll take cover in a field till it gets dark enough to travel."

I had a case of nervous jitters walking through town, but Bryn and Dave seemed nonchalant and we reached the jungle without incident. Fortunately it was vacant, and in less than five minutes we found three empty moonshine bottles. We took them with us when we headed north in the cover of the trees beside the creek.

At times the creek wandered as much as two hundred yards from the track, but it always came back, and three miles north of town we left it and flattened out in a grain field until dark. Meanwhile, we had rinsed and filled the bottles with water. We were hidden from view in the grain stalks, and it wasn't long before my partners were asleep. But even though I counted sheep, sheer excitement kept me awake till the sun went down. After dark, when Dave woke me up, it was from a dream of the Saskatchewan prairie. It was late fall, the grain had been threshed and I was in the middle of a stubble field with a twelve-gauge shotgun under my arm and a brace of prairie chickens hanging by their necks from my belt.

The dream was so realistic that when I heard the words, "Come on, laddie, it's time to hit the trail," I thought I was being wakened by my uncle to feed the horses and start the fall plowing. But when I woke, I realized where I was with a sharp stab of nostalgia.

Thinking the highway and railroad might be watched, we ate before crossing the grain field to a side road, which we followed till the first sign of daylight. Then we hid in another grain field about seven miles from the border. We were thankful we'd heeded Bryn's advice about taking water from the creek, since it was a scorching afternoon.

When we crossed the border at 2:00 the next morning, it was dark and foggy, and we blundered into the Emerson graveyard. Wending our way between the headstones was eerie, and when I tripped over a low marker and fell on a grave I nearly panicked. If I'd been alone I'd have raced out of the graveyard smacking into headstones in my haste to get rid of the ghostly place. But seeing how frightened I was, Bryn said calmly, "I'm starving. Let's eat here." I nearly gagged.

"I'm hungry too," I murmured, "but eating here would be sacrilegious."

"That depends on how you look at it," Dave said. "The stiffs won't hurt us, and they might enjoy having guests for an early-morning snack. That ghost bullshit is a legacy from medieval times. It scared people then, but this is the twentieth century, kid, and those old wives' tales don't scare anyone now. Let's eat here, away from the prying eyes of the town clown. Then we'll circle the burg to the water tower. It's only five or six miles north, and everything stops there for water."

I remembered what I said in the Hallock can: I was still a passenger. I nodded. And after a few hesitant bites I ate my beans with relish. I was glad we'd eaten when we got to the water tower two hours later. In a nearby grove of Manitoba maple trees we flattened out and pounded our ears until awakened by a freight. We grabbed it and slept all the way to Winnipeg.

CHAPTER 7

IN THE MID-1920S, WINNIPEG WAS HARD PRESSED TO claim two hundred thousand inhabitants, but I, still a small-town boy, was overawed. To me, the six- to ten-story buildings looked like skyscrapers, and I had a hard time acting nonchalant.

On Portage Avenue, Dave and Bryn waited on the street, while I went below to an underground can for a leak. I thought it vacant until I heard a toilet flushing. I turned and spotted a pair of straight-last shoes peeking from under a door. The large, nattily dressed, blond wearer of the shoes came to a basin beside the latrine I was using, rinsed his hands and made a pretence of combing his hair while looking me over. He asked, "Is Winnipeg your home?"

"No," I said.

"That's a pretty good handful of meat you got there. When's the last time you had a woman?"

I thought he was a kook, but I didn't want to be rude. I buttoned up my fly and headed for the stairs before saying, "It's been a while."

The guy caught up to me, stuffed his comb in his pocket and asked, "You been in town long enough to find a place to stay?"

"Not yet, but I'll get one. I'm gonna be here a few days."

"Maybe if you had a job you'd decide to stay. I own a small factory, and I could use a young man like you. Why not let me buy you a good meal and tell you about it?"

The job offer stopped me at the foot of the stairs. My bankroll of six bucks had to feed and bed me until Bert got sprung and arrived in Winnipeg. True, he had proof of citizenship before we crashed out of the can, but now it was in the hands of the American and Canadian bureaucrats. There was no way of knowing how long it would take to process and deport him, especially if some stiff-necked, red-tape obstructionist found some technicality to hang his hat on—and both governments were overstaffed with these self-righteous dimwits.

Although I needed the job, there was a phony ring to the guy's approach. I wasn't about to ditch my mates on the word of a guy I figured bogus. So, going upstairs I said, "Okay, but there's two guys I met on a freight from Portage waiting upstairs for me. I'll tell them you're going to take me to dinner and give me a job."

"That's good. I'll wait while you tell them."

Had I been around enough to know the score, the knowing looks on the kissers of Dave and Bryn would have warned me to tell the guy to fuck off. But in my innocence I thought they were happy for me when Bryn said, "Well, go ahead, but if things don't work out you won't have much trouble finding us if you check the flops on skid row."

Heading to a good meal and a job within an hour after hitting Winnipeg should have been cause for elation. But something about the guy tied my guts in a knot, causing me to keep looking back for a glimpse of Bryn and Dave on the three-block walk. But when we entered the café they weren't in sight.

The restaurant was large. And the meals, most of which I'd never heard of, were so expensive I was afraid to order. Noticing how the menu intimidated me, the man took over and ordered a porterhouse steak with the trimmings. Even before the soup came he started firing questions. I knew he was trying to get a read on me, so I parried with yes or no answers that told him nothing. Meanwhile I put the make on him.

Finally he said, "For the time being you'll stay with me, but I want it understood that I don't allow women in my quarters, because they're troublemakers. That may seem hard to a handsome young lad like you, but they're not the only sex outlet there is."

That put enough numbers on the slate for me to get a make on the fake Samaritan, weighed alongside the bull-session tales I'd heard at Hallock. The guy was a wolf.

Like most active boys I was a big eater. I hadn't eaten since the 2:00 a.m. snack in the graveyard, and then there'd been the long morning walk from the rail yards to downtown Winnipeg. I was wolfing down the dinner till the numbers suddenly hit the slate. When I added them up, my appetite went.

I put down my knife and fork and clammed up until the wolf

62

smiled. "Eat up, lad. I've nothing important on this afternoon. So when we finish I'll take you to a movie. Then we'll have a good supper before I take you home."

Hearing this I suddenly clapped my hand over my mouth as if I was bilious. Faking a vomiting fit, I held my hand there and puffed my cheeks out like a pouter pigeon. Then I ran for the door. I got to it just as a couple were leaving. He had the door open, and the woman, about to step through, saw me coming and stepped aside. I bolted through the open doorway, then sped down the street to get as far away from the wolf as I could. But before I even got fifty yards a pair of brawny arms wrapped around me and hoisted me clear of the sidewalk. They forced the air out of my lungs and almost stopped my heart. I was struggling weakly to free myself when a voice in my ear said, "What's the rush, Legs?"

When I turned my head, Dave was grinning. So was Bryn behind him. "Jesus Christ," I gasped. "You guys scared the living shit out of me. I thought it was the wolf that put the clutch on me—cause that's what the sonofabitch is. But hell, I looked back a block from the crapper, and you guys were still standing there. When did you decide to tail us?"

"We never had anything else in mind," Bryn said, "but we wanted to give you enough rope to hang yourself. We had the guy pegged for an asshole bandit and knew you'd put the figures on him when he started making passes. But we wanted to be handy when you told the big prick to fuck off."

When we started down the street the wolf was apparently still in the restaurant. I pictured him waiting impatiently for me to throw up and return.

I had a cup of coffee while Bryn and Dave put away a feed of pork chops at the nearest greasy spoon. They were still picking their teeth when we signed the register in a four-bit flophouse. Bone weary, I was all for hitting the blankets. But when Dave and Bryn washed their shirts, socks and underwear, then showered, I did the same.

When I lay down, I thought I'd be asleep before my skull smacked the pillow, but my mind had other ideas. It began rehashing the events of the past five weeks. The prairie visions I saw through the door when the train was leaving Saskatoon reappeared, and I was doubting the wisdom of leaving home for pie in the sky when sleep sank my reflections. When Dave shook me awake to go for a late supper, I left the blankets unwillingly.

After a hamburger, we were having a smoke with a coffee, when Dave said he was going to grab a freight in the morning for northern Ontario.

"You should come with me, Bryn. You could file on a homestead in a country so picturesque it's an artist's paradise. The land there's so rich it grows the best wheat in the world. I'd ask you to come too, Legs, but you're too young to file on a homestead, and I know you promised Bert you'd wait for him here."

"You make it sound pretty good," said Bryn, "but I'm not a farmer, and I don't think I'd make a go of it. Besides, I've still got my mind set on going to the States. In the morning I'm heading for Windsor. I should be able to get a rumrunner there to take me across the river. I'm still packing enough dough to pay for that."

We were still shooting the shit in the small lobby of the flophouse when Bryn spotted me yawning. "You better hit the pad, Legs. As a matter of fact, we better all sack out if we expect to get an early start in the morning."

Again, I had trouble going to sleep, but the thoughts keeping me awake concerned the present, not the past. How long would I have to wait for Bert? How far could I stretch my four-dollar bankroll? How long would it take to get a job pearl diving? These and other doubts kept me wide-eyed till early morning daylight. When I woke up, both Bryn and Dave were gone. Not knowing then it's a hobo trait to avoid sentimental goodbyes, I felt small and unimportant because they didn't wake me up and wish me luck before leaving. So I took a shower. It helped. By the time I'd dressed and put away coffee and doughnuts, I stopped feeling sorry for myself and started thinking about what I had to do.

A bo directed me to the post office, where I bought a penny postcard and addressed it to Bert Mercer, General Delivery, Winnipeg, Manitoba, giving him the name of the flophouse where

I was staying.

On the way back from the post office I kept a sharp eye out for "Dishwasher Wanted" signs in the café windows. Then, less than a block from my flophouse, I spotted one outside a hash house. I thought I had hit the jackpot, until the Greek owner told me he'd already hired someone but had forgotten to take the sign out of the window.

Disappointed but not discouraged, I went to the flophouse and paid for another night's flop. The clerk had no change. So I told him to keep the buck as I'd be staying another night or two.

Since I intended to look for a dishwashing job after the noon-hour rush, I had two hours to kill. I spent them in the flophouse lobby, watching two men play checkers, until I got tired of seeing the better man toy with his weak opponent. Then I picked up a morning paper someone had left on the table and riffled through it until I found the Help Wanted page. But when I found no laboring jobs listed, I went up the street to a pool hall.

The only man in the room besides the houseman and five shooters playing pea pool on the front table was a sandy-haired character with enormous feet and a lemon-sized Adam's apple that bobbed up and down every time he breathed. He was watching the game from one of the chairs against the wall. I sat beside him and got a friendly nod. He pulled a pack of smokes from his shirt pocket and gave me one before lighting up himself. Then he asked if I wanted a game of snooker.

I thanked him for the tailor-made, but refused the offer. "I'd like to play," I said, "but I don't know how to hold a cue."

To put me at ease he smiled and said, "I don't play very well myself, but I like the game. Haven't seen you around before. I'm from Toronto, myself. Came west for the harvest last fall and planned to go back when it ended. But I couldn't stay out of the poker games, and I couldn't win either. That's why I landed up in Winnipeg broke, with snowballs pelting my ass. Since then I've been peddling bills and doing odd jobs, trying to put enough scratch together to get a new front and go home."

After the loss of Dave and Bryn I welcomed his friendliness. I was about to open up and tell him where I came from and how I happened to be in Winnipeg, when a guy with a mustache plopped into the chair beside me and said, "Jesus, I'm bushed. I never got a wink of sleep last night, but did I have a night." And he pulled out what I learned later was a boodle—a phony bankroll with a sawbuck wrapper—bigger than a wrestler's wrist.

"Christ, man!" Bigfoot said. "Put that away before someone sees it and puts the arm on you. It ain't smart to flash a roll that big in a place like this."

"Don't worry," said Mustache. "I been around enough to know how to take care of myself. I won it in a poker game last night, and there's lots more where it came from. I'm a gambler. I never turn down a bet if the odds are even. Where the hell's the can in this joint? I need a piss so bad my tonsils are waterlogged."

Bigfoot told him it was in the basement, and when the guy was out of earshot he said, "Guys like that give me a pain in the ass. He thinks flashing a roll of bills makes him a big-time operator, but all it does is set him up to be taken. When he comes back we'll get him to match for dough. You take heads and I'll take tails. That way one of us will win every time, and after we take him we'll split the take."

I shook my head, saying, "I better not. I've never gambled."

"But you won't be gambling, son. You can't lose. You're not gambling when you can't lose. You're the first guy I ever met that wouldn't bet a cinch. What the hell you got against making an easy buck? Are you so well heeled you can't use some easy cash? The stupid bastard's asking for it, so don't be as dumb as him and let your morals stop you from picking up a few bucks."

When he said this he pricked my pride. Like everyone, I had a touch of larceny, and the thought of clipping the wisenheimer didn't jar my conscience. So I nodded and said, "Okay."

When the gambler came back he never got his ass in a chair before Bigfoot said, "You're not the only one gets his kicks gambling. I'd turn down a rumble with a luscious broad to go to the track or a poker game. If you're gonna be here a while, the three of us could match coins for a few bucks to kill time. Whaddaya say? Odd man takes all."

The gambling man pulled out a quarter, flipped it carelessly in the air, and said, "Suits me. Name your poison. How much you wanna play for?"

Bigfoot then asked me, "Are you game to play? If you are, how much do you want to play for?"

I pulled out a buck and said, "Yeah, I'll play, if one of you gives me change so I'll have a coin to match with. Two bits suits me."

"Two bits?" the gambling man snorted. "Hell, man, that's not money. Let's play for something worthwhile. I'm not a penny-ante gambler."

Bigfoot was quick to retort, "Two bits may seem like peanuts to you, but everybody's not a big-time gambler. Let's toss for a quarter this time. Then you can call the shot. Then I'll call it. If we take turns calling the shot, everyone can have a say in how much we play for, but let's put a buck on a toss."

We tossed for a quarter. I won. Then the gambler called the shot. He called a buck. Bigfoot won. He called the shot for half a clam and won again. He was up two bucks and six bits on the gambler and me. A buck and six bits was the gambling man's dough, and a buck was mine. We went around again with the same result, and after another round Bigfoot had my three bucks, including the quarter I was flipping.

I knew my going to tap city would break up the game, but what the hell, I'd be up three clams when I got my end from Bigfoot.

I got it all right, but it wasn't six bucks. Bigfoot and the gambling man were short-con artists, and I'd been taken for my last three bucks. But it didn't end there. Bigfoot had the winnings in his duke, and when I told them I was clean the gambling man said, "You sons of bitches are in cahoots. You set me up, but you won't get away with it." Then he grabbed the winnings from Bigfoot's hand and belted me in the jaw with an overhand right before dashing out of the pool room with Bigfoot on his tail—as if he was trying to retrieve our dough. And I suddenly realized I'd never see either one again.

After spending the afternoon tramping the streets on an empty gut looking for "Dishwasher Wanted" signs and finding none, I returned to the flophouse despondent, tired and hungry, my spirits lower than a midget's ass in hell. I took a seat beside an old bo with a stubbled kisser sucking a toothpick. I was not in a talkative mood, but I listened when the old timer unloaded his troubles on me. He'd been on a two-week drunk when the law picked him up for being drunk, and he'd been in the can for three days before going to bat and being freed that morning by the judge.

Proof that the old saw "misery loves company" has merit. I countered by telling him my troubles. My tale brought a chuckle from the old bo before he said, "Son, what you were bucking is a con game older than Moses. It's called 'the smack.' It gets its name from the belt in the jaw that the mark gets when the con men have him clipped and have to blow him off. Knowing how you feel, maybe I shouldn't say this, but you got what you asked for when you let a stranger talk you into helping him clip another stranger for a quick buck. You got off cheap. Three bucks and a day's hunger ain't much to pay for what you learned. It ain't the end of the world. You won't starve, 'cuz there's good people on the street. All you gotta do is go out there and keep telling people you're hungry till you find one that'll feed you."

When I told the old bo my troubles I wanted sympathy, not a lecture. But what he said gave me a lift, and I thanked him before hitting the street to beg. The first guy I approached was sorry but broke. The next one shot me a scornful look and snapped, "You look big and healthy enough. Go to work." And when the next three guys gave me the tin ear, not even looking at me when I spoke, my hunger lost the round to my pride and I went back to the flophouse empty in pocket and belly.

Hoping sleep would give me relief from the ache in my grumbling gut, I hit the sack when I heard the carillon on a nearby church chime nine. But when my eyes closed I thought about sitting at my uncle's table gorging myself on a sumptuous Thanksgiving dinner with all the trimmings. I heard the midnight chimes before I slept.

The next morning I had to use all my willpower to overcome the urge to ask for the four-bit advance I'd paid the flophouse. Had I not feared I'd miss Bert when they dumped him in Winnipeg, I would have. Having given up hope of seeing a dishwasher sign I walked aimlessly throughout the morning. I finally sat on a bench in a park. I can't say how long I'd have stayed there feeling sorry for myself if a grandmother with a small child hadn't arrived with a bag of stale bread and begun feeding the squirrels. Watching the aggressive critters get the crusts and the timid ones the crumbs convinced me I had to master my timidity and ask for a handout or starve. I left the park determined to get fed.

I went into a café and asked for a job washing dishes. The answer was no. So I went to another. After getting the same reply, I decided to change my approach. In the next one I asked to see the owner, then asked him if he had any work a man could do to earn something to eat, telling him I hadn't eaten for two days.

The owner, a fat, middle-aged Italian, smiled and said, "This is going to make Dino happy. He's my kid. Twice a week I make him come in after school to peel potatoes and scrape carrots. Go in the kitchen and tell the cook to feed you. Say I said so. Then tell him to show you what to do. When you're finished come see me before you leave, okay?"

The cook sat me down to a feed of meatballs and spaghetti, and I ate my fill with a glass of milk before he took me to the basement where the vegetables were stored. I had to peel two bags of potatoes, scrape a bag of carrots and wash each one before putting them into large shortening pails. In three hours I was done and went upstairs, where the cook fed me again. On the way out I saw the boss. He went to the cash register and took out a dollar, which he handed me. "If you're still in town and not working, come back in a couple of days and we'll make Dino happy again."

Now that my gut was full it suddenly hit me that I'd never gone without food for so long and had taken good meals for granted. It would never happen again.

Ever since I was six and my fingers were strong enough to squirt milk from a cow's tits, I'd worked hard with pride. But that feeling fell far short of the sheer satisfaction I had when leaving the restaurant with a full gut and a buck in my pocket. Not for the three hours I'd spent peeling spuds, but because I'd taken the initial step toward faring for myself on the road—and knowing I'd never go hungry again.

That evening I was reading the paper in the lobby when two working stiffs came in. They were on their way to a railroad dirt job, and when they began talking about it I got on the eary because it sounded like a good job for Bert and me to head for when he arrived. I asked them how far the job was from town, how much the contractors paid and if they hired on site.

The skinny guy with the pockmarked kisser sneered and said, "If you're thinking of going, it's a might far from here to Assiniboia, and the job's southwest of there. I know they're hiring on the job, and they're paying sixty a month and found. But I don't know what they're paying bull cooks and water boys, or whether they're hiring any."

I was glad to get the information, but resented the smirky bastard's assumption that I couldn't handle a team of horses hitched to a dump wagon. I felt like telling him I'd cut my teeth on a lead line and when it came to handling horses I didn't have to back up from him or any man. But I kept my lip buttoned and went to my room.

Next morning I got up early, ate breakfast, then pounded the streets looking for a pearl-diving job. But expecting Bert to hit town any time, on a hunch I had told the desk clerk I expected a caller and would be back at noon.

Bert was reading the paper when I came into the lobby and didn't see me. When I nudged his shoulder with an elbow he turned, jumped to his feet and was aiming a chop at my guts when he saw who it was. "Christ, Legs," he exclaimed, then laughed. "You startled me. I got your card this morning. Sure was glad you made it. Where's Dave and Bryn? They staying here too?"

"No. They left town the morning after we got here. Dave went to his homestead, and Bryn took off for Windsor. A friend of his from Australia lives there. He's a rumrunner, and Bryn hopes he'll take him across the border with a load of booze."

"Let's go have a coffee," said Bert. "Too many guys on the eary in here, and I'm anxious to hear how things went after the three of you took off."

I kept a bridle on my curiosity until the flophouse door closed behind us. Then I beat Bert to the punch with my questions. "What happened when the sheriff found out we'd broken out? How much lead time did we get? What reprisals did the sheriff take?" Bert held up his hand. "Whoa, boy! Hold it! One at a time. I can't answer them all at once."

"Okay, but tell me about the sheriff first."

Bert gave a little chuckle. "I'll get to the sheriff later. The real excitement happened when the three of you were in the woodpile. You remember the old guy called Moses—who was always praying and trying to convert everybody? He went hairy when he found out you guys had smashed out, and started shouting for the sheriff. So we all drowned him out by singing wobbly songs." But then, Bert said, Moses whipped off his red shirt, ran to the window with the bar out and started waving his shirt to attract attention. Josh and Bert grabbed him and threw him to the floor, but the old bastard wasn't as frail as he looked. When they figured they had him subdued and let go he came off the floor swinging like an Irishman and dropped Josh with a lucky punch, laying a pigeon egg under his eye. Then Bert lost his temper, and laid Moses out with a right to the jaw. They carried Moses to the padded cell, but he came to while they were locking him in.

Eventually, the deputy came to open the doors for the café runners, heard the uproar and asked what was going on. When everybody dummied up, he charged upstairs and found the ranting Moses—who instantly blabbed about the jail break.

"Fortunately for Josh and me," Bert added, "by the time the deputy inspected the window, locked the corridors and fetched the sheriff, Moses was so incoherent he fingered everyone in jail. So the sheriff racked everyone but Moses back for two days.

"As for lead time," he finished, "I'd say locking up Moses gave you a three-hour start before the sheriff knew you were gone. Now tell me what happened after you left till you crossed the border."

So I did.

CHAPTER 8

WE WERE IN A GREASY SPOON DRINKING COFFEE when I finished my story. Bert said, "The farmers won't be taking on any hands till harvest. We should check the railroads to see if we can ship out to a gandy job till then." I nodded and told him I'd heard two dump wagon skinners talking about a job southwest of Assiniboia, where they were hiring on site.

"Did they say how much they're paying skinners?" Bert asked.

"Sixty a month and found."

"Sounds good, if there's any truth in it. Assiniboia's only about four hundred miles west. If we pull the rag out, we can start today and check the yard offices in Brandon and Moose Jaw to see if they need any gandy dancers. If those skinners know what they're talking about we'll run into hobos or skinners in the jungles between here and Assiniboia who'll know where the dirt job is. I'd rather go there and smell horse farts than tamp ties with a banjo or swing a twelve-pound spike maul for less money."

I felt like a five-year-old kid admitting he broke the cookie jar when, on the way to the west yard, I told Bert how I got clipped by the short-con artists. He laughed and said, "You bought a cheap lesson. It could of been a harvest stake. Now you'll think twice before trusting a smooth-talking stranger. There's an old saying that makes a lot of sense: 'A man that has no larceny in his blood can't be clipped.' Think about it."

The only men in the west jungle were four canned-heaters, who were wringing alcohol from four cans of sterno through a dirty red bandanna and were too incoherent to tell us what was happening anywhere. So we got the hell out in a hurry.

In Brandon we met two Ukrainian gandy dancers heading for work on a CPR extra gang eighty miles west of Estevan, Saskatchewan, near the American border. With this news we headed southwest, and three days later I made my first acquaintance with a banjo, more commonly known as a shovel.

At first, the repetitious work with no mental effort, coupled with the blisters on my hands, made the hours seem painful and tedious. But in a few days, when the blisters callused and I started envisaging better things to come, I began to enjoy the camp's ribald humor, and the Sunday gab sessions were as enjoyable as those in the Hallock County can. But I was not very happy with the grub Crawley McCracken, the camp's catering firm, dished out.

The camp was shorthanded when we hired on, and it remained so until the haying season ended. Then farmers' sons from both sides of the border began hiring on. Bert and I became friendly with two brothers from Montana—strapping, square-jawed lookalikes named Hub and Ned Ferris. Their father, Percy, owned and farmed three sections of land bordering the 49th Parallel, and on Saturdays, when the evening chores were done, he'd crank up his Model-T Ford and come to the camp to take Hub and Ned home for church and Sunday dinner with their large family—three teenage daughters and four boys. After the meal, the family would retire to the parlor for prayers. After giving thanks to God, Ned and Hub helped Percy do the chores before he cranked up the Model-T and took them back to camp.

The farmers and townspeople living on the U.S.-Canada border all considered it only an imaginary line and treated it as such. They visited back and forth, attending county fairs, church socials and barn and school dances on both sides with little hindrance from the law.

Two weeks after Hub and Ned came on the job they asked Bert and me to spend Saturday evening and Sunday with their family. We declined reluctantly, because I had on the only clothes I owned, and though I kept them as clean as I could, they'd become shabby.

On the first of every month the crew gathered in front of the railway office car after work, where the time clerk stood in the doorway calling out names and doling out checks. Although you had to wait till your name was called until you got paid, there was always a great deal of pushing by the working stiffs anxious to get their pay and spend it.

The few family men walked to the general store and post office a mile away to mail money orders home. The gamblers—and there were many—bought only tobacco and enough small goods to make it worthwhile for the merchant to cash their checks and leave them the balance for a poker stake. The lushes always concerned the super, because they pocketed their checks and grabbed the first freight dragging through the campsite for Moose Jaw to get liquored up—and many of them were key men doing special jobs. My first pay went for a pair of shoes and some new duds, so Bert and I could cash in on Hub and Ned's offer.

When we finally arrived, we were awed by Percy Ferris's holdings. Neither Hub nor Ned had mentioned the size of the family's acreage or the sprawling, well-maintained buildings. The two-story fieldstone house had six bedrooms. The kitchen, with a giant pantry off it, was big enough to hold a homemade pine table that sat twenty people with elbow room. The barn stabled 112 head of horses and had an attached cow shed. The granary, machine shed and other buildings were frame, with a recent coat of scarlet paint. In the yard between the granary and a forty-four-inch McCormick Deering threshing machine stood a steam Case tractor, and behind them in neat rows sat the mobile bunkhouses, the kitchen and the dining wagons.

When Bert saw the size of the threshing outfit he said, "That's one hell of a big separator and steam engine. Your dad must thresh all the grain in the country."

"Not quite," Hub answered. "But there's a hell of a lot of neighbors depend on us to thresh their crops, and a lot more would like us to, because my dad makes sure that most of the grain goes in the grain tanks and wheat bins, and not the straw stack. The grain will soon be ready for cutting, and when it is you and Legs should quit the railroad and work for my dad. He pays top wages. He always hires two binder men and six shockers to take the crop off, and keeps them until the last grain of wheat comes down the grain spout."

So three weeks later Bert and I, plus six other working stiffs, bedded down in one of the two bunk wagons and ate our meals off the large kitchen table with the Ferris men. The home-cooked slabs of beef, garden-fresh vegetables and fresh fruit pies were a far cry from the tasteless Crawley McCracken grub. Bert, the four Ferris brothers and I cut the crop, which was stooked in windrows ready to thresh by the six harvest stiffs who followed the six binders.

By then, most of the neighboring farmers had their harvesting done as well, and sent hired hands with teams and hayracks to help Percy thresh his crop. When we finished, everyone hopscotched from farm to farm to thresh the neighbors' crops. This meant no more of Mrs. Ferris's cooking, and Percy hired a camp cook for the mobile kitchen.

The big Case steamer had a straw rack attached to it. It was fired by straw and stoked by a fireman with a three-tine fork. Bert got the fireman's job, which paid an extra buck a day, and I drove a bundle team.

A wet fall caused numerous delays, extending the usual time to thresh the Montana crop by two weeks. It was the final week in November before the last straw flew out the straw blower, and all hands except Bert and me were paid off. Percy Ferris kept us on for another ten days to help him and his sons haul and stack thirty acres of oat sheaves for horse feed.

It was the seventh of December and still no snow except for a few slight flurries. But when Hub cranked up the Model-T to drive us sixty miles to Glasgow where we could catch a freight east on the Great Northern, the sky filled with snow clouds. Halfway to town fluffy white flakes began to swirl, and before we got there an inch of snow had fallen. Hub had intended to eat with us before heading home, but because of the storm he decided to leave before the roads drifted over. We helped him put on the chains at the train station, and he bade us goodbye.

Watching the Ford disappear in the whiteness I experienced feelings of loneliness and sadness similar to those I felt the day my stepfather separated me from my sisters and pawned me off on relatives.

When the car disappeared Bert said, "I know what you're thinking, Legs. I used to feel the same when I said goodbye to a friend, knowing I'd never see him again, but I learned to shrug it off. You will, too, when you've had as many partings as I've had.

Come on, let's go eat. You'll feel better once you get outside a steak."

I saw the wisdom in what Bert said, but my spirits were still low when we reached the café. Bert had his say and was smart enough to steer the talk to our planned trip to Chicago. By the time I finished putting the T-bone away I was talking about the trip with enthusiasm.

After eating, we bucked our way through the storm to the jungle, where four bos drinking coffee were huddled around a fire. One of them told us they were headed for Minot, North Dakota, and were waiting for a redball that had a meet here with a westbound passenger train. According to what the dispatcher told him, the through freight should be in the hole already. He had hardly finished giving us the information when the big roadhog's warning whistle shattered the air.

At 2:15, when the eastbound freight pulled onto the main line, the temperature was around zero—and falling. By nightfall it had plunged to eight below. The other four bos in the boxcar were more warmly dressed than we were, but we all paced the car, flapping our arms and stamping our feet to keep from freezing.

The train pulled into the Minot yards at 8:30. Luckily there was no bull in the yards, because the cold had chilled us so much our legs were too stiff to jump off the moving train. The walk uptown in the swirling snow convinced us to spring for a $3.50 hotel room, where we could thaw out in a steaming tub before eating.

The next day we bought warm clothes before catching an early freight to Fargo, North Dakota. There were no empty boxcars, so we boarded a gondola with three other bos.

Nearly three hours out of Minot the train stopped at a small tank town to refill the water tender. Then twenty minutes after it got under way, three men wearing blue denim combination overalls came from the head end on top of the boxcars and climbed into the gondola. We were sitting on our packs with our backs to the front of the car and didn't even hear them till the lead guy clambered in.

Nobody spoke till they squatted on the steel floor a few feet from where the five of us were sitting. Then the smallest of the three asked, "You guys been threshing on the same rig?"

We were a little apart from the three bos, and Bert answered quickly, "No, my buddy and I are coming from Seattle. We're on our way home to Chicago. We've been on a sight-seeing tour of the southern and western states since school closed last summer."

The little guy shed his mitts and said, "Yeah, I bet you have." Then he stuck his hand inside his overalls, pulled out a flashlight and beamed it on us. "You're pretty goddamn well decked in warm togs for a couple of punks that's been on the bum all summer. But we'll soon find out if you're telling the truth."

Then he rammed his free hand inside his bulky combinations, yanked out a .38 Colt automatic and leveled it on Bert before he started moving it slowly back and forth, covering the five of us. Then he snarled, "If any of you guys is dumb enough to do something stupid, like trying to buck this gun and put up a fight, he's gonna lose more than his harvest stake. Get on your feet and turn around. Raise your arms as high as your shoulders, stick them out in front and hold them there until my mates finish fanning you to see if anyone's packing a heater."

Satisfied we were clean, the little guy's mates singled out one of the bos, turned his pockets out and came up with a fair-sized roll, which they counted aloud before handing it to the guy with the gun. It was sixty-three bucks. The next bo didn't get off easy either, for when the thugs shook him down and all they came up with was forty cents and a half mickey of moonshine, they worked him over with their fists, knocking him down, putting the boots to him—and then killing the moonshine themselves.

Watching the hijackers clobbering the bo because he wasn't packing put the shit up my neck. And though it was still eight below I began to sweat. By the time they got to me I expected the same treatment, because Bert had made sure that I kept only a couple of dollars in my kick.

Returning to the hotel with our new duds we had stopped at a bank and exchanged our small bills for big ones. Then Bert bought a small roll of adhesive tape at a drug store. In the room we changed clothes from the skin out, but before putting the long underwear on we taped the large bills to our thighs, keeping only enough money in our pockets to get by on.

When the hijackers handed my pittance to the little guy with the rod without working me over, I thought I had it made. Secretly I was feeling smug because of Bert's knowledge of hijackers who worked freights in the harvest season and preyed on unsuspecting stiffs with their stakes in their pockets. Also, when the hijacker asked if we all harvested on the same rig, I gave Bert marks for saying we were students, not working stiffs.

My smugness was short-lived. These guys were pros and knew the ways of hobo working stiffs. After they shook Bert down and came up dry too, the little guy with the gun said, "These punks ain't school kids. They been around enough to know how to look after themselves. It don't make sense. Two punks can't spend the summer bumming around without working and be decked out in new clothes from head to foot. They probably got their harvest stake pinned to their underwear, or in a tobacco sack tied to their nuts. Have a look inside their clothes all the way to their skin." They made Bert and me sit down and take off our boots and socks. When they found nothing there, they made us stand barefoot on the steel floor and drop our strides. When we did, they grabbed our long johns, peeled them down to our knees and found our stake. By then my feet were numb with cold. I would have put my socks and boots on before pulling up my pants except for the thought of sitting bare-assed on the steel floor.

The other bo, a loner, was smarter than Bert. He had outsmarted the hijackers before he left Minot by banking his stake. But when the hijackers found his shiny new bank book with a recent single entry of three hundred and seventy dollars, one of them whipped out a nickel-plated heater that must have weighed two pounds and pistol-whipped the poor bastard before thrusting the book in his kisser. "You wily son- ofabitch," he shouted. "Before I'm through with you, you'll wish you'd never heard of a bank. You're gonna eat every goddamn page of this fucking book, and I'm gonna salt and pepper every goddamn bite you take with this heater. Every time you take a swallow I'm gonna belt you with it in the jaw."

The big goon ripped the pages from the bank book and rolled them into a ball the size of a pigeon's egg. Then he waved his heater under the shaking bo's nose and told him to open his mouth. When he did the big goon rammed the wad into it so hard it gagged the poor bastard, and the ball shot out of his kisser. The poor bo, fearing a pistol-whipping, dropped to his knees and scooped the wad off the floor quicker than a hawk on a field mouse. The three thugs thought it hilarious. I can't say whether the laugh proved a deterrent, but the big goon put his heater away.

Ten minutes later when the hogger cut the throttle and the train began slowing down for a meet, the little guy leveled his rod on us again and said, "This is as far as you guys go. You're getting off here when I tell you." We lay in the hole shivering for twenty-five minutes before a passenger train whizzed by, but the little guy with the gun kept us on the train until it was back on the main line and starting to ball the jack. Then he stood waving the rod and said, "Which of you assholes is going to be the first to unload? This is the end of the line."

Bert was the first off. I followed the lush, whose nose was still dripping blood, and by the time the poor bastard that got pistol-whipped hit the dirt the train was going faster than he could run, ground-looping him into the ditch. Fortunately there was enough snow to cushion his fall.

Under different circumstances, seeing the bo do a cartwheel would have been amusing, but Bert and I were too concerned about his well-being. We ran to the ditch to see if he was badly hurt and help him if we could. But the other two bo's got to him first, and the guy was on his feet no worse off than before he took the header.

We were in the middle of nowhere. The only building at the siding was an unused tool shed with its door locked by a big brass padlock in a steel hasp. At the rear we found two rusty oil drums without tops and full of holes, evidence that they'd been used for braziers. We carried them to a nearby woods, where we set them about twelve feet apart before firing them with dry branches from surrounding deadfall. When the fires were lit, we dragged two logs between them to sit on.

Since leaving the train, we had to forget our losses and figure a way to get through the freezing night without serious frostbite. Finding the barrels was a lucky break, and everyone pitched in and worked so hard there was no time to talk about our woes. But now that the job was done and our exertions had restored circulation, we sat on the logs in the warmth of the fires, goofing off about what happened on the train. When they found out Bert and I wouldn't go to the police with them and lay charges against the thugs, the bos got pissed off and dropped the subject. No way were we going to get tangled up with the law this close to the border.

Like the others I kept nodding off every so often. We got through the night without getting too cold, and at the first sign of daylight we heel-and-toed it to the nearest town.

By ten o'clock we were walking down the short main gut of Hannaford, hungry enough to eat a skunk's gizzard, but more intent on getting out of town before the bos told the cops that they and two other guys had been robbed and kicked off the freight train by three armed thugs.

The town was too small to have a police force, but was only eight miles from Cooperstown, the county seat, and would be under the protection of the state police stationed there. Like similar hamlets, however, it would have a town clown, who, on hearing the hobos' tale would pick us up and take us to Cooperstown to tell our version. Fearing a repetition of what had happened in Hallock, we never broke stride until we were three miles beyond town, hoping one of the few cars traveling the gravel road east would pick us up.

We had to gamble that if we got a lift it would be a native who didn't suspect we were aliens. It helped that the hobo harvest-end migration was in full flight. The mid-northwestern states were overrun with itinerant working stiffs beating their way to winter bush work and railroad construction camps, plus many more heading for big towns or cities to hole up until it was time to recrop the land. Many more were also traveling south to duck the snowballs.

Over the years the natives had become inured to the annual influx of these itinerant workers, and they could almost tell by the calendar, within a day or two, when the migration would start and end. But when the crops were harvested and the labor force was no longer needed, the law took over and harassed the hobos to keep them moving until the migration ended.

Two hours and six miles out of Hannaford we passed a farmer beside a roadside mailbox. He gave us a friendly nod as we passed, but I only took three or four strides before I stopped, retraced my steps and asked him, with a stammer, if he could spare something to eat for two men who hadn't eaten since yesterday.

When he didn't respond I thought I was getting the tin ear, but when he finished fishing the mail out and snapped the flap shut, he turned and said amiably, "I reckon I can. But that's not for me to say. That's the wife's department. Call your friend and we'll go up to the house and ask her."

When we entered the kitchen the farmer's wife was taking fresh bread out of the oven, and the toothsome aroma gave me another shot of nostalgia. My mother was baking and my sisters and I were sitting at the kitchen table, greedily relishing hot bread liberally smeared with butter and plum jam. To cover welling tears I faked a cough and yanked out my handkerchief. I clapped it over my nose, and kept snorting nothing but air into it until I was under control.

When the farmer told his wife that Bert and I hadn't eaten since yesterday, she pursed her lips and tut-tutted before saying, "Well, we'll have to do something about that. Move up to the table. I'll start you off with a bowl of bean soup. It's been simmering on the stove for hours and it's ready to eat."

We tore into the soup and hot bread like hungry bulls at a haystack. Before the bowls were empty the compassionate woman had a mouth-watering spread of food on the table, and while we were gorging ourselves on pork chops and vegetables, topped off with a large slice of apple pie, she made us a lump for the road.

To give generously and not humble the recipient is a gracious art few people acquire. Yet the farmer and his wife were so adept at putting us at ease that we were able to thank them humbly and sincerely and leave without humiliation.

The farmer told us it was fourteen miles to Pillsbury, but the town was so small that all the trains except the way freight and local passenger went through it like a raccoon outracing a coon hound. It was after dark when we got there, but we still had two hours to kill before the local came through on its way to Fargo. There was no jungle in the town, but we scrounged a five-pound lard pail and two tobacco tins in an alley. After we knocked on a couple of back doors, a woman gave us almost half a pound of coffee. Armed with this we went down the tracks beyond the town, brewed coffee and ate the lump the farmer's wife had given us. Then we went to the station and sat near the possum-belly stove until the natives began arriving to take the train to Fargo.

The weather was still hovering around zero at ten after ten when we left the head end of the passenger train in Fargo and made our way through the yards to the sand house, where we spent the night sleeping on the warm sand. In the morning we washed in the roundhouse change room, then checked the call board and saw that a southeast train was leaving for Minneapolis at 11:20 a.m. This gave us plenty of time to hit the stem and mooch the price of breakfast and a sack of Bull Durham before catching the southeast train.

We arrived in Minneapolis without getting frostbitten—but that was only because, for every mile the train traveled, we logged a mile jogging inside the boxcar. We gambled on the night being cold enough that the yard bull would be toasting his shins beside the office stove instead of prowling the yards. The railway cop knew most bos hole up anywhere they can find a place to keep warm in sub-zero weather, but he wouldn't buck the cold himself. We went to the roundhouse and asked a locomotive fitter if we could have a shower to thaw out.

Chilled to the bone, we stayed in the shower twenty minutes and would have stayed longer if two hostlers hadn't come into the locker room for coffee. We had put our long johns on the steam rad with our boots and socks beside it, so they'd be warm when we dressed again. We left the shower, went bare-assed to the rad and were getting dry from its heat when one of the hostlers nodded toward the hot plate and said, "When you get dried off and dressed, pour yourselves a coffee."

"Thanks," I said. "It'll warm us up inside. We goddamn near froze to death holding that redball down from Fargo, and our guts aren't thawed out yet."

Thinking of the hot coffee shifted me into high, and when I had everything on but my boots and socks, I went to the hot plate and poured Bert and myself mugs of coffee.

Bert grabbed his cup, took a swig and said, "Jesus, men, that's good. It's warming me all the way to my navel. Now let's hit the stem, Legs, to get the price of a flop."

I winced at the thought, but said, "Okay, but I'm sure as hell not looking forward to begging the price of a flop."

The hostler who'd been silent till then said, "You can sleep in the cab of one of the engines. There's two or three engines in here that ain't gonna turn a wheel for a week or two. You'll be clear of the yard bull. He never checks dead engines for sleeping hobos." So that's what we did.

In the morning we hit the stem, and soon got the price of doughnuts and coffee. But by then we'd decided it was too cold to travel. We'd find a warm place to sleep and hold Minneapolis down till the weather warmed up. With this in mind we set out for the sand house, but on the way we passed the rip track—a dead end spur track—where old or damaged railway cars are repaired. The repair gang had a fire going in an old caboose, which they were using to warm up and have smokes.

Two men came out of the heated crummy pulling their mitts on and two more went in. Bert pointed to the wisp of smoke coming out of the chimney and said, "There's our flop. We'll bed down on cushions tonight. It's my guess those workers keep a pot of coffee brewing on the stove. And you can bet your ass they'll bank the fire for the night before going off shift. If the yard bull sees smoke coming out of the chimney, he won't give it a second thought."

"How do you know they won't lock it before they leave?" I asked.

"What for? There's nothing in there to steal, and the rails know bos aren't vandals; so there's no reason to lock it. Anyway, an ordinary skeleton key'll unlock it, and we'll get one if we have to."

For the next four days, when we weren't panhandling or putting the beg on restaurants and hotel kitchens, we kept out of the cold by dividing our time between a public library and a pool room. Nights, we bedded down in the warm bunks of the crummy. On the afternoon of the fifth day the weather began to warm up, and on the following morning it was once again fit to travel.

CHAPTER 9

TWO DAYS LATER WE WERE HEEL-AND-TOEING IT UP State Street in Chicago south of the Loop—the old business district. The Loop was just a short walk from the four skid rows, but like all the homeless that made Chicago their stamping ground, I seldom went near it. Mostly we haunted the skid rows. And there were thousands of us.

In the early twenties Chicago was served by upwards of forty railways, making it the largest railway center in the nation. Trains came from and left for every point of the compass each hour around the clock. And the city had more welfare agencies and better medical aid for migrants than any other in the country.

These facilities—plus the fact that the harness bulls pounding their beats were far more tolerant in dealing with itinerants than police in other large cities—made Chicago a haven for hobos, tramps, oddballs, mission stiffs, home guards and cripples.

The city's homeless population seldom dropped below thirty thousand, and it doubled after freeze-up when every incoming freight brought drifters to the city searching for a winter haven.

Hobos arrived with their summer stakes and good intentions of buying a new front and finding cheap winter lodgings before giving the whores and blind pigs a play. But all too often the good intentions gurgled down the drain in a day or two. Inevitably, their first purchase would be liquor. And when they got drunk they became instant prey for moochers, gamblers, pickpockets, jackrollers, pimps and larcenous whores. Then they'd wake up broke in an alley or the doorway of an abandoned building.

The tramps (who never work) came to Chicago to scrounge off drunken working stiffs and drink up their stakes whenever they could latch onto one who hadn't yet gone to tap city. If a tramp failed to find a live one, he'd hit the stem and beg the price of a flop and something to eat. If he failed to bum enough to take care of both, he'd eat and carry the banner.

The mission stiffs came to the city to exploit its many Bible-thumping missions. They'd be the first to beat a path to the pulpit when God's kindly recruiters made their pitch for the Lord and asked all who wished to seek Jesus to come forward and be saved. Then they'd spend the winter on their knees, because an ungodly stiff had less chance of getting a bed and fed than a God-fearing one.

The floaters and home guards lived and got by in four Chicago areas they called stems. The traits of the different stems' inhabitants gave each skid row an identity of its own. West Madison Street, the main stem, was larger then the others. It stretched west for about a mile and a half from Canal Street before petering out a few blocks west of Morgan Avenue.

Two blocks west of Canal on both sides of Madison, footloose working stiffs, tramps and home guards could satisfy all their needs at the various two- and three-story emporiums along Madison. Cheap hotels and flophouses, beaneries, cheap restaurants, barber colleges, missions, gypsy fortune tellers, second-hand shops, cheap-clothing stores, saloons, drugstores and gambling joints either offered needed services or separated the street's unwary nomads from their hard-earned stakes.

Scattered among these shops were the numerous employment agencies—called slave markets—that working stiffs were reluctant to patronize because they believed no one should be allowed to sell jobs. Generally, they only used them when they wanted to ship out to distant jobs. Then, for a two-buck fee, they could ride the cushions free for several hundred miles to the job site.

A further peculiarity of this stem was that the only women there were rubbydubs, never sober. Too slovenly to peddle sex, they got by on the handouts of undiscriminating working stiffs who turned a blind eye to these slatternly lushes and bought them booze or a meal for their favors.

The State Street stem running south of the Loop to Twelfth Street had a smattering of family life. But it had no appeal for restless, footloose youths who made their stamping ground the main stem and only went to State Street occasionally, looking for a cheap thrill at its burlesque theaters and female barber shops.

State Street's main inhabitants were the savers, home guards and Great Lake sailors, who favored the area because the hotels, flophouses and boardinghouses were cleaner and, for only a few cents a day more, offered better amenities than those of the other stems.

Savers were the hobos who husbanded their summer stakes to pay bed and board for the winter in one of the cheap hotels and lodging houses on south State, Van Buren or Clark Street. The home guards were working stiffs that lived in the city year round, but only worked one or two days a week, or short-hour day jobs, to meet their needs. There was a noticeable difference between the bos and home guards who lived there and those in the other skid rows. Their clothes were less grimy and they shaved every day.

The skid row on Grant Park's lakeshore, stretching from the Field Museum to Randolph Street, was only a five-minute walk from the Loop. On warm sunny days itinerants went there to read or listen to old-timer raconteurs tell stories. Those who carried the banner stretched out on the ground to sleep.

The park had an undeveloped area behind the Field Museum where industries dumped their scrap. Old hobos who found life on the road too tough to cope with, plus a number of home guards, scrounged discarded material from the dumps and built crude shacks. Men went there to fish, bathe and wash clothes while mulligans boiled on open fires.

North Clark Street below Chicago Avenue was the stem where hobo intellectuals reigned. Here footloose artists, poets, writers, dreamers, thinkers and agitators rubbed shoulders together. Washington Park was the center of this stem. The bums called it Bughouse Square, because on warm days and evenings many of the habitués mounted soapboxes and harangued their audiences on everything from religion to revolution.

At times there would be three or four speakers at once postulating their different theories. They all had audiences, and only a few listeners heckled, whether they agreed or not.

Bert and I worked the street, panhandling every likely-looking guy we met. By the time we hit Bughouse Square we had pocketed three dollars and change and had a run-in. That's when the guy you beg from takes you to the nearest restaurant and buys you a meal. Then, invariably, he sits there firing questions that you field as dextrously as a politician dodging darts at a press conference. Pleased that, despite the delay and hardships, we had finally reached Chicago with enough cash in the pot to scrape by on, we stopped and listened to a Bible thumper touting the Second Coming while a skeptic heckled. But we soon tired of listening and went to the skid row at West Madison and Morgan. There we paid for a night's flop, had a shower and washed our dirty clothes, before hitting the pad to catch up on the sleep we lost on the train.

I woke up at 8:30, dressed, went to the cubbyhole where Bert slept and pounded on the door to wake him. After he dressed we had a wash before going downstairs to Jack's Beanery, where we got a large bowl of beans and a coffee for a dime. Then we crossed the street to a pool room where a ten-cent pea pool game was in session. We watched for a while before Bert, a better-than-average shooter, took a stick in the game, which lasted until midnight.

Then with Bert in pocket a buck sixty from the Kelly game, we walked east to an all-night movie on Madison and Halstead. Many bos that only had a nickel and would otherwise have had to carry the banner used to spend the night there. And I got a bang out of watching the two guys patroling the aisles with long bamboo poles to prod the snoring bos awake.

On the way to the flophouse after the show we put away a fifteen-cent feed of bacon and eggs. It was nearly 4:00 a.m. when we rolled into the blankets, intent on getting up at six to go job hunting. But when we woke it was after ten and too late to look for work. So Bert decided to take another whirl at pea pool. After filling up on beans at Jack's, we crossed the street to the pool room.

The only lights were over the first table, where two guys were playing Boston—a pool game where the lowest ball on the table must be hit first. The Greek owner was brushing one table briskly with a brush in each hand; all the others still had green dust covers on. The Greek looked up when we entered, recognized Bert from the previous night's game and came over. Then he nodded toward the five guys sitting along the wall, watching the Boston game. "You see the guy with the green and gray windbreaker? I don't know how good he is, because I never saw him before, but he's looking for a game. How about playing him a few games for the house?" When Bert agreed, the Greek went back to the table he'd been brushing, turned on the lights and racked the balls. Then he went to the next table, folded its dustcloth and began dusting again.

While Bert and the guy in the windbreaker were shooting straight pool, other shooters and onlookers straggled in—the shooters to get into a pea pool game and the others to escape the cold. At three o'clock the Greek asked the Boston players if they'd mind using another table. They grumbled until the Greek said the next two games were on the house. So, cues in hand, they plucked their bennies from the wall hooks, went to another table and broke the balls.

The guy playing Bert was a pretty good shooter, but Bert handled him easily. At no time did he have to open up to stay far enough ahead to win, but still not far enough in front to discourage the guy. They were still playing at three-thirty when the pea pool game started.

I could tell by Bert's kisser and the way he looked at the shooters on the front table that he was pissing his pants to get in it. But, out of loyalty to the Greek, he kept playing. Then the guy in the windbreaker looked at the wall clock, hung up his cue and said, "Thanks for the game. I'd like to play more, but I go on shift at four o'clock."

Ready to eat, we walked to the door with Bert's pool partner. He went west and we went east looking for a greasy spoon. After eating, we went back to the pool room. When the game broke up shortly after midnight, Bert had ground out enough dimes to get us by for a couple more days.

We were up at six and spent the morning job hunting. We filled out job applications at three factories, but had to put the flophouse address and phone number on the forms, which gave us little chance of hearing from them if they needed factory hands.

After lunch, when we entered the pool room the Greek was bent over behind the tobacco showcase, restocking it from cartons scattered on the floor. When he recognized us he reached into a carton, tossed a double deck of Bull Durham to Bert and grinned. "Your friend in the windbreaker's back for more punishment. Play him a few games of house pool. It'll kill time for ya until the pea pool game starts."

It turned out the guy in the windbreaker was a good guy to know. He answered to the handle of Gus Bardon and was shop steward for the printing union in a large printing shop. When he found out Bert had come to Chicago to get a job and learn a trade he gave him a note to the business agent of the Chicago local. So Bert got a swing-shift job in a printing firm.

The only hitch was that the company paid weekly and held back a week's pay—meaning it would be two weeks before Bert would see a cent. Meanwhile we had to find a way to get by, because Bert was on afternoon shift and couldn't buck the pea pool game. I had a plan in mind, but I didn't tell Bert because I wasn't sure I had enough guts to swing it.

At three the next afternoon, after Bert took the streetcar for work, I set out to see if I was man enough to bum enough scratch for us to get by. I walked Madison west well beyond skid row before I put the beg on anyone. Three hours later, after countless snubs, tin ears and blasts for being a bum, I wound up west of Crawford Avenue with three bucks' change in my kick.

Bert finished his shift in time to get to the pool room before its one-o'clock closing. I was watching the door as itchy as a four-year-old waiting to tell his dad he'd found a nest with baby robins in it. But after months of experience, I curbed my exuberance when I told Bert. Still, he was delighted.

"Well, you clever little bastard," he grinned, smacking my back.

We went to the pool room after a late breakfast. It was closed, and one of the regulars hanging around the door said, "The joint's still locked." As we turned to leave, we saw the Greek climbing off the streetcar. He unlocked the door, the regulars trailed him in like ducklings behind their mother and Bert and I followed. When the Greek saw Bert he came over with the table brushes and asked if we'd give him a hand to uncover the tables, brush them and rack the balls before he collapsed in a chair.

He said he'd had a bad turn during the night, and the doctor had told him that morning he'd have to cut down on his working hours. He then asked Bert if he'd open the pool room, do the cleaning and run the place until he arrived at two. Bert said he'd like to but was working swing shift at a print shop. So then the Greek asked me. He would pay, he said, two bucks a day. I grinned, and stuck out my hand.

The Greek took a key from the cash register and handed it to me. "There's no need to come in before eleven o'clock opening time," he said. "You'll have lots of time to do the cleaning then, because more men come early to get out of the cold than to shoot pool."

I was as pleased when I pocketed the key as I was on my sixth birthday when my grandfather took me to the barn and told me my present was in the box stall. And when I looked in I saw the pinto pony.

The thought of running a pool room by myself three hours a day, seven days a week, had me so pumped up I hardly slept. But lack of sleep didn't keep me from leaving the sheets in time to knock back a good breakfast of bacon and eggs and turn the key in the pool room door by a quarter to nine the next morning.

But it wasn't for business. With the door locked behind me, I hurried through the room to the last table, folded the dustcloth neatly, took the rack off the balls, grabbed a cue from the rack, broke the balls and never stopped practising until eleven.

At two o'clock the Greek came in and asked how things were going. When I said as far as I knew everything was aces, he went to the damper, punched the No Sale key and took two bills from the drawer. "It looks like you've got everything under control. I'll see you tomorrow, unless you eat and come back to play house pool?"

I stuffed the bills in my kick, and said, "Thanks. I'll be back to hang around. But me playing house pool would be a losing proposition. I'm a very poor shooter."

The Greek bit the tip off a cigar and spit it out before he said, "Don't let that worry you. No matter how badly a man does what he does, there's always someone that can't do it as well."

Now that I no longer had to hit the stem, I practised daily, concentrating on cultivating a good stroke, the proper weight and a firm bridge. Within ten days I was doing well enough to play the average shooter and hold my own. From then on my game improved daily, because now that I was stroking the cue well, I spent my mornings learning to control the cue ball.

Bert was on day shift when he got his first pay. That night we rented a room on Monroe. It had a hot plate, sink, and enough dishes, pots and pans to cook a meal. From then on I did most of the shopping and cooking. But the red-letter day was on Bert's second pay.

Bert had cottoned to a lanky, tousle-haired workmate named Laurie Wier who came to the pool room with Bert that Friday and found me bucking the pea pool game. "Come on, Legs," said Bert. "Hang up your stick. We want you to come with us."

It was the first time I'd taken a stick in the game, and I didn't want to quit because I was holding my own with the big shooters. "Where you going that's so important I gotta go too?"

"Okay, wise guy," he grinned. "So stay. But when you find out what you missed out on, you'll kick your ass from here to State Street." Then he gave Laurie a poke and said, "Let's get goin'. I'll tell wisenheimer where we went after we get what we're going after and get back."

The waggish grins on their kissers pricked my curiosity so much that I racked my cue, grabbed my jacket and tailed them out the door. "Well look who's decided to tag along," cracked Laurie. "Do you think we should give him a second chance to get laid? After all, he turned it down once."

"Laid! Who said anything about getting laid? You assholes simply walked into the pool room and told me to rack my cue. Nothing was said about getting laid."

"So now that you know," Bert laughed, "you still coming or are you chickening out?"

The thought of seeing the inside of a whorehouse was exciting. "Sure I'm going. That's if you don't think the madam'll mind me waiting while you and Laurie get laid, because I don't have the price of a piece of gash."

"She won't mind," Laurie said. "But you're gonna get a bang too. It's only a deuce a jump, so if you're not squeamish about breaking your maidenhead in a whorehouse, Bert and I'll put up an ace each to get you laid."

I was hesitant, but Laurie's reason had nothing to do with it. What put the shit up my neck was that ever since I'd been on the road I'd been listening to guys bragging about what good studs they were. I'd heard them say, "If you don't know how to fuck you might as well jerk off. A piece of tail's more than climbing on and banging until you blow your load. You gotta know what you're doing, or the woman won't respond. And if a woman doesn't respond, a piece of tail is no better than pulling your wire."

But there was no way I was going to stay behind. There were four girls in the large front room of the notch joint when the madam bade us welcome. The room was furnished with a stuffed horsehair sofa and six upholstered chairs. A table against the wall held two slot machines that one of the girls was playing. The three other whores were huddled together on the sofa.

To cover my nervousness I made a wiseacre crack that one of the girls found demeaning. She called me a smart-assed punk trying to show off. I wanted to strike back with another retort, but realized I was overmatched and kept a lock on my kisser. So I sat red-faced until Bert gave the madam a deuce and told me to pick a broad.

I chose the youngest of the four girls. She was a little blonde that looked younger than me, and when she took me to the trick room and closed the door, I was stupid enough to ask why a young girl like her was working in a whorehouse. She bristled and said, "I hear that question from every smart-ass that comes in here. I'm nineteen and I'm sure that's older than you. But for your information, I like what I do for a living, and I've been doing it since I was sixteen. Before I found out I could get paid for it, I fucked a fortune away."

When she left the room and closed the door behind her I thought I'd blown it and tried to think of what to tell Bert and Laurie when they asked how I made out. But the whore came back with a pitcher of hot water, put it on the washstand beside a basin and said, "Why you standing in the middle of the room with your clothes still on?"

My face turned redder than a baboon's ass from embarrassment, and I started fumbling with my belt buckle. Then forgetting I had to take my boots off to get my strides off, I let them fall around my ankles. By the time I finally got my boots and strides off, the whore had taken off her shift and was flat on her back with her knees up and spread.

Awed by my first sight of a naked woman, my eyes and jaw both popped. I was standing there like a stunned ox when she said, "Aren't you going to do anything but gawk? Are you one of those nuts that get more charge out of looking at a naked woman than screwing her?"

"No," I said, trying to control my stammer. "It's just ... you're the first woman I ever saw naked. I never had a woman before. That's why I'm acting this way."

"Why didn't you say so sooner? I wouldn't have lost my temper when you asked dumb questions. But come on, I'll make up for it when I take your cherry."

To add to my embarrassment I blew my load on the third downstroke. But the young whore showed compassion. When she was washing my joint with hot water and I boomed up again she said, "You came so fast neither of us got much out of it, but I see you're ready again. If we hurry we've got time for another. Since I was so uppity, I'll give you a free ride. But we better get started. If we take too long, old Rosie will accuse me of giving you a double-header and holding out her end. Then I'll have to give her my end of the one you paid for." Then she smiled, "By the way, if you come back again, my name's Bella."

The next trick didn't take very long either, but long enough that when Bella and I came out of the trick room, Bert and Laurie were already in the parlor. "What took you so long?" Bert grinned. "Couldn't get it up?"

I tried to think of a glib retort to wipe the smirks off their kissers, but Bella butted in. "He's not like you two jack rabbits. He knows how to give a woman a thrill, and he doesn't do that jumping on and off before she's had a chance to come, too."

That sobered them up fast. Not another word was said until we got outside. Then Bert asked, "Tell the truth, Legs. Did you really make the bitch come?"

"You heard what the lady said. And by the way, I told her who gave me the money. And she said to thank you for her, too."

CHAPTER 10

BERT'S NEW SENSE OF ACHIEVING SOMETHING HAD changed his outlook on life. He began writing home weekly, and the letters in return became the highlight of his week. Every time he got word from home I got a lecture censuring my indifference to the work ethic. He would harp about my being content to get by without doing anything constructive. His pet speech was, "You can't go through life without leaving something worthwhile behind. There's no satisfaction in being a taker. You gotta have a meaningful purpose for living, or your life is wasted. Get out and get yourself a job. That's what you came to Chicago for, wasn't it?"

His constant harping finally got to me, and after fanning my ass for three days diligently tramping the factory areas, I landed a job operating a punch press in a small sheet-metal factory. For two solid weeks I endured the monotony of putting a metal blank in the die of the press, tripping a foot treadle to activate the ram and ejecting the formed product with a hand lever. Then I suddenly pulled the pin in the middle of a shift.

Bert was on afternoon shift when I got home with the news that I'd quit because boredom was driving me hairy. He stopped making sandwiches for work, slammed the bread knife on the table and stared tight-lipped with piercing eyes before he started shouting. The blast he gave me cut so deep it sent me scurrying around the factory areas that same afternoon. Two days later I got a job in a creamery bulling ten-gallon cans of cream from trucks onto a loading platform, then hand-trucking them inside to be tested for butterfat.

Then three weeks after I started in the creamery, Bert got an upsetting letter from home. His eyes shone like polished sapphires when he started reading, but he was fighting back tears after he began. "Bad news?" I said.

For answer he handed me the letter. The first paragraph was cheerful, but the second was a preparation for the bad news that followed. Bert's father had suffered a stroke. He would live, but his left side would be paralyzed for life. Bert's mother was putting the farm up for sale because she couldn't afford to hire help to run it, and his brothers were all too young.

"I'm sorry," I muttered as I handed back the letter. Then I added, "I wish there was something more I could say to ease your grief."

He pocketed the letter and nodded. "Thanks, Legs. I know you mean well and would like to help, but this is something I have to do myself. I can't let Mom sell the farm. I'm going home and work it. I'll be on the cushions on the first train for Winnipeg tomorrow. With my back pay and this week's wages I'll have money for the fare and pocket money."

I hate goodbyes, and I was glad when Bert insisted that I not miss a shift to see him off. Bulling cream cans off a truck was mindless work that required little concentration, but at least it was safer than the press shop, where amputations were common. If I'd still been working there my moniker would probably be "Fingers" now, not Legs.

After Bert left, Lanny, a fat, redheaded can heaver, moved in. He was three years older than me, but far younger in smarts. Working at the same job was all we had in common. He was a loner who spent his time going to movies and reading western magazines. Unintentionally I changed that. On pay day I took him to the whorehouse and introduced him to sex. From then on he patterned his life after mine.

I tolerated working in the dank, smelly atmosphere of the creamery until March. Then one day I yielded to the beckoning finger of the bright spring sun. I quit on the spur of the moment, and when I told Lanny he pulled the pin too.

Lanny's quitting to go with me created a problem I hadn't counted on, for he was bent on coming along when I left Chicago to search for work on a farm or dirt camp. Lanny was born and raised in Chicago, and the only horse he'd ever seen was hitched to a milk or bread wagon. But I took him with me and hoped things would work out.

We grabbed the head end of a C. and A. passenger heading south out of Cicero. Three days later, in the jungle at Fort Smith, Arkansas, we heard there were a number of road construction camps in Oklahoma, near Muskogee, that were hiring dump wagon skinners. We spent the night and part of the next day getting there, and hired on at the first camp we came to. Our job as dump wagon skinners was to haul dirt from higher elevations to fill the low spots in the road. Each wagon, pulled by a team of horses or mules, carried nearly two tons of dirt in a box behind, which the driver could release with a lever.

Hauling a dump wagon on soft ground in hot, sultry weather is hard, sweaty work, especially for the horses. An ill-fitting collar or unclean shoulders will cause massive shoulder sores on any animal that has the misfortune to be driven by a greenhorn skinner. Knowing this, when the corral boss showed us the teams we'd be driving, I decided to go between mine to check their shoulders for sores. Before I did, though, I spoke to them softly and patted their rumps.

When I went between the mules, Lanny thought it was the thing to do, and headed between his team without a word or a warning pat. The mules, which were as nervous and skittish as Lanny, hunched together. This put the fear of Christ in Lanny, and he bolted out of the stall.

The corral boss, an old-timer, told him, "This ain't no job for greenhorns, son. The fill's twenty-five feet high, and the grade when they're filling a ravine could be twenty feet. Even good mule skinners are hard-pressed to dump their wagons at the edge. Mules are smart animals. They know if a wheel goes over the edge they'll wind up at the bottom of the fill—a tangle of harness, wagon and guts. You best come with me to see the cook. He tells me he needs a new bull cook."

The long hours Lanny had to work bull cooking didn't bother him. In fact, he liked the job and was hoping some day to become a camp cook. That's why, when I pulled the pin two weeks later because the camp was lousy, he stayed on.

You could say my wanderlust really started then. For the next two years, I zigzagged all over the States and Canada, crossing the border numerous times but never keeping a job for more than two or three months. I had no fear of being broke, for I had the stem and back doors to fall back on. I can't exactly put my finger on when my thinking began to change, because it was gradual, but I think it really started two years later.

CHAPTER 11

I HARVESTED IN KANSAS IN 1924. FROM THERE I went to Montana, then to Canada, where I, and other harvesters took the whiskers off Jack Canuck at Biggar, Saskatchewan. Luckily the harvest wound up in time for me to catch a freight and beat the snowballs into Chicago. Chi was to be a one-night stand, long enough to get a good night's sleep and a soak in a tub before taking the C. and A. south for the winter.

I got a room in a flophouse on Madison Avenue. It was a series of five-by-ten plywood cubicles covered by chicken wire, crammed together on the second and third floors above three stores. Each cubicle had a cot, but no light, except for the dim glow of the amber lights in the ceiling high above. The walls were so thin you could hear your neighbor breathe. The guy in the next crib, a loud teeth gnasher, woke me up. I hadn't a clue what time it was: no watch, no windows. I was still tired, but the gnasher was now cursing, either from a nightmare or too much derail. Between the curses and clashes of his ivories, my room was no place for a sky pilot. I debated whether to stay in bed and curse the bastard back or get the hell out. I got.

Bare-footing it to the washroom with my razor, toothbrush and skimpy hotel towel, I thought maybe the son of a bitch had done me a favor. After getting cleaned and dressed, I'd eat and take the El to Cicero, where an early morning train might be leaving for the south. If I took it I'd be a hell of a long way down the line by dark— New Orleans, here I come!

There was a man in the washroom when I went in, a skinny hawk-faced guy about my age. He was washing a pair of heavy woolen socks in one of the three concrete laundry tubs screwed to the wall. The hotel provided these to stop the working stiffs from doing laundry in the sinks and bathtubs. The skinny guy looked up and smiled. "How ya doin'? It's a hell of a storm out there, ain't it? How long you think it's gonna last?"

"Storm?" I said. "What the hell you mean, storm?"

"Christ, Mac! Ain't you bin outside? There's ten inches of snow on the street, and it's still coming down. I tell you that old guy up there's been dusting us all night, flakes bigger'n thumbnails. Go take a gander and see for yourself."

I went to the window and nearly fell on my ass. There wasn't a sign of life outside. I knew by the unbroken blanket of snow that traffic hadn't moved for hours. Jesus Christ! I was snowbound. Why the hell hadn't I batted right through to Springfield? But then I thought about the El. It would still be running, but I'd have to wade through a foot of snow to get there.

"You're right," I said. "The old man's been busy all right. I wish I'd highballed it right through here yesterday. Goddamn it, I'd a been halfway to St. Louis by now. Got any idea what time it is?"

"Yeah," answered the hawk-faced guy. "I just saw the clock in the lobby. It's about five . . . a little after. There ain't no papers. I guess they couldn't get through to deliver them. If you're not in a hurry to get to St. Louis, you can make a buck shoveling snow. After I finish up here I'm going to Canal Street and hire on. If you want to come along I'll show you the ropes."

"Well, hell," I shrugged, "why not? How far we gotta go to scoff?"

"Just out the door. There's a one-armed joint on the corner that's open around the clock. I gotta get my coat and hang these socks in my room. I'll wait for you in the lobby. By the way, my friends call me Boots, but the handle my folks gave me's Percy Peerce. At school the kids called me Pee or just plain Piss, and that got me so goddamn mad I'd take a poke at any guy no matter how big he was. Made me a good fighter for my size. If you're headed for St. Louis when the snow job's over, maybe I'll join you."

"Yeah," I said, shaking his hand. "I guess that would make a fighter out of most guys. They call me Legs. With monikers like ours we shouldn't have any trouble plowing our way to Canal Street. I won't be long. I'll just brush my teeth and skip the shave."

While Boots was buttering his toast in the café, he asked, "Where you from, Legs?"

"Me? Saskatchewan. I'm a stubble jumper from a small town outside Saskatoon. I left the prairies five days ago when the harvest wound up."

"This the first time you've been in Chi?"

"Hell, no. I wintered here two years ago with a buddy, but I don't want any more of that. It's too goddamn cold and windy. As soon as this fucking storm stops I'm heading south and staying there till spring."

When we finished our bacon and eggs I grabbed the checks. "No need to do that," said Boots. "I got a coupla bucks. Yesterday I had a deuce on a horse that paid four to one. That's enough for a week's rent and a few bowls of soup."

"It's okay," I said. "I'm still packing what's left of my harvest stake, but I want to be long gone before it peters out. What time do they start hiring? D'yuh think we should get going?"

"Yeah. If we get there ahead of the mob we can get in out of the cold." Boots then told me how to get paid for shoveling snow without shoveling any.

"I didn't tell you before, because I wanted to find out if you're a right guy or not. But listen. When we line up to get hired, be sure you stick with me. That way we got a good chance of getting in the same gang. If we don't I'll watch out for you."

This was how it worked. When you signed up you got a slip of paper and a numbered tag. The slip was for the foreman—you gave it to him when he called your name. Then you took the tag to the guy dishing out shovels. He'd take the tag, give you a shovel and hang the tag on a nail with the same number as the tag. When the shift was finished, you returned the shovel and got your tag back to get a shovel for another shift. But those with smarts knew that every foreman would take money, and then piece off the shovel wrangler. So when I got my shovel I was to give it to Boots with the slip and a buck and a half. The buck was for the foreman and the four bits were for the guy in the crib riding herd on the shovels. When Boots gave the foreman the money and shovels, he'd stash the shovels in the truck's cab, and we would piss off.

"Y'see?" Boots said after he'd finished his explanation. "No snow. No sweat. Sounds complicated I know, but it ain't. The foreman looks after everything. All we gotta do is be there when the truck comes back so we can get the shovels from the foreman to get the tag back and get shovels for the next shift.

"The foreman spends most of his time sleeping in the cab, so he works every shift. Which is good, because we only have to deal with one guy—or two, if we work two shifts at the same time. And we'll work two. When I piece off the foreman we'll line up again using a different monicker and go through the same thing over and over. There's a hell of a lot of snow fell. If we're lucky, we could get three two-day shifts around the clock. That's thirty-nine cartwheels a day. More'n a hundred clams."

"Here," I said, handing him three bills. "For that kind of dough I don't give a damn if it hits forty below. I'll stay here and freeze. But when we hire on, I'm getting out of that fleabag we're staying in. I'll find a place where I can cook my own grub and don't have to listen to that teeth-grinding bastard."

Slugging through the knee-deep snow was tough going, but less for me than Boots. I was wearing a pair of fourteen-inch Leckie logging boots. But Boots, despite his name, had on only a pair of ordinary tan brogans that filled with snow before he took three steps. By the time we got to the big stone warehouse from which the city ran the operation, his feet were nearly frozen.

The place was closed, but the yard and streets were jammed with dump trucks. Fifty or sixty men were milling around a door, flailing their arms and stamping their feet. Many were hunched over hugging themselves to stave off the cold. We got as close to the door as we could before Boots, balancing on one leg like a stork, pulled his left shoe and sock off and dropped them in the snow. Then he pulled a dry sock from his pocket, put it on the bare foot, shook the wet snow from the shoe and put it on.

"Feels better already," he grinned. "I'll be fine when the other one's done."

"Jesus Christ, man! I've seen gutsy things, but you're the wildest. You better hurry and get the other one done before they open the door and the stampede starts."

By the time Boots finished changing his socks there were five hundred working stiffs champing at the bit to get inside. All hell broke loose when the door finally opened and everyone tried to get through it at once. Those at the front began shoving, which caused fists to fly. But despite the bedlam, the men jammed through the door four abreast carrying Boots and me with them. Everyone queued up in front of one of six tables inside the big warehouse. Each table had two clerks. The first clerk asked for my name and address and a telephone number—which I didn't have. The other clerk gave me a slip and a tag, then pointed to where they were handing out shovels. The guy in the tool crib took the tag, gave me a shovel, then pointed to an archway and said, "Go through that alleyway. You'll see the gangs being formed. You're in number-six gang. The foreman's name is Carter. When his truck's ready and he calls your name, go to the truck."

I had the shovel, but was sweating it out waiting for my name. I'd lost Boots in the crush, and I worried whether I had enough tact to handle the foreman. Then I spotted Boots heading for me. When he got close enough to be heard in the din he asked, "Who's your foreman?"

Relieved to see him but still worried about whether the game would work, I blurted out, "A guy named Carter. I'm in gang six. What gang you in?"

A grin split his narrow face. "No worries, old buddy, we're in the same gang. We got it made. I had Carter last year, and he's an okay guy. When we come back at four, I'll bring him a pint of moon. When I offered him one last year, he was embarrassed, but he took it and thanked me. So what the hell. It only cost thirty-five cents."

His grin broadened. "When Carter calls our names you better come with me and meet him. Just in case I don't show for a shift, it's better if he knows who you are."

We stood against a cement pillar watching gang four load and leave. The men rode in the dump box. To facilitate loading, portable wooden stairs were pushed beside the truck. While this was happening, number five's foreman rattled off the names in his crew. As their names were called they gave him the blue work slips, and huddled beside him.

Then a huge red-nosed man in a khaki parka charged out of a

small office. The fingers clutching his board were as thick as my shovel handle, and his hands were almost as big as the blade. I was thinking I'd hate to get an open-hander from this guy when Boots nudged me. "There's the big bastard now," he said. "Ain't he something? That's Carter."

As Carter called out names, his roar almost muffled the barking exhaust of the trucks. The men went quickly toward him as their names were read, their shovels slung over their shoulders like soldiers on guard detail. "Pete Hawkins." The name caromed off the walls of the room.

"Come on, that's the phony name I gave when we signed up," Boots said, nudging my ribs. "Look at those stupid bastards marching up to Carter like he was a sergeant-major. Christ almighty, he's all bark no bite."

Before we reached Carter, my alias, "Bernard Brice," was called. Boots handed Carter the work slip with three ace notes folded inside. Carter clipped it to the top of the clipboard with the rest of the slips, and gave no sign of recognition. But when he finished the roll call, he maneuvered Boots to one side where they talked briefly before he headed into the office. Boots came back and took me aside.

"What's up?" I asked. "Something wrong?"

"Not really. Carter took the dough, but he's a bit leery. The word's out that an inspector is on the job, so he says we gotta load with the crew. He doesn't care where we get off, as long as we ride out of here and leave the shovels in the truck. We're gonna have to move fast when we pull out if we're gonna get in line again.

"Now get in the back of the truck so you can jump off easy. It stops for a second when it gets to the street. Before we get there I'll crack some line and jump off. You do the same, then fan your ass back inside. If we get split up I'll see you in the archway again. Yuh got it?" I nodded.

After leaving the yard in the truck Boots snarled, "Fuck this. I'm not dressed to work in his weather." Handing his shovel to the guy beside him, he said, "Will you see the big guy gets this?"

I took the cue. "Christ, Bud," I said. "You got a point. Give him this one too, Jack." And we quickly clambered over the tailgate.

The second time around was a breeze. We high-tailed it back to the hall and queued up in a different line. Choosing a different alias, we went through the previous routine and were heading for the skid row in half an hour. The sidewalks were still not cleared, but people were now walking on well-trodden ruts.

Boots bought a paper at Canal and Madison, but when he couldn't open it with his mitts, he said, "Let's stop at Halstead and grab a coffee. I want to look at the scratch sheet. Maybe something good's running."

"Suits me. I'll have a gander at the rooms for rent while you're putting the figures on the ponies."

We took our time, sipping coffee and dragging on wheat-straw Duke's Mixture smokes I rolled for us while Boots tried to put together a three-horse parlay. It didn't take me long to tick off three possible light-housekeeping rooms on Washington Boulevard. I didn't mind waiting for Boots to finish handicapping the entries. In fact, I was getting an education listening to him talk about past performances, sires, dams and jockeys. When he finished making notes on a napkin with a stub pencil, he crumpled the napkin and stuffed it in an empty cup. "That's it," he said. "There ain't anything going today I'd bet on. How'd you make out? Find any good rooms?"

"Yeah, three over on Washington, between Curtis and Sangamon."

"Well, let's get started," said Boots, jumping up. "If we can't find a nag, let's look for a roof."

CHAPTER 12

WHEN NOBODY ANSWERED THE BELL, BOOTS SAID, "Maybe the goddamn thing's not working. Try knocking."

I rapped on the door without taking my mitt off. "Christ, man," he said, "they'll never hear that. But if there's anyone in there alive they'll hear this"—and he played a tattoo with his foot.

"The hell with it," I finally said. "Let's try the other houses. We'd gone down the steps when a voice behind us rasped, "What the hell yuh trying to do? Break the door down? Can't yuh give a body time to answer?" The shivering old crone that belonged to the voice tugged a worn woolen shawl around her shoulders. "If it's a room you want, I ain't got none. I rented it last night."

"Sorry, ma'am." I said. "I thought you might be on the third floor, not able to hear the bell. That's why I banged the door so hard. I'm sorry you haven't got a room to rent."

The next address was eight doors west. It was the only house on the street that had the steps and walks cleared of snow. I thought this should be a clean place. The people didn't mind a little extra work.

A diminutive, gray-haired old lady wearing metal-rimmed glasses opened the door. She was neatly dressed in a long black skirt and a blouse trimmed with a tight-fitting white collar. Draped over her tiny shoulders was a man's huge woolen cardigan.

"Good morning, gentlemen," she chirped. "Though I must say it's not. Are you here about the room?"

"Yes, ma'am. If you haven't rented it, may we see it?" I asked.

"Of course. It's on the second floor. You'll like it. It's a nice big room with a sink and a big front window facing the boulevard. The bathroom's only two doors down the hall at the top of the stairs. It's a good room. I'm sure you'll like it."

She kept selling the merits of the room while climbing the stairs like a gazelle. There must be a fountain of youth, I thought, and this old lady's been there.

The room reflected the character of its owner. It was large with a high ceiling and a big bay window hung with worn lace curtains yellowed from age and use. A patterned red and black carpet covered the floor. All the furniture in the room, except the table and chairs, was ornate, hand-carved mahogany that had once been handsome. Now it bore cigarette burns and white whisky stains from every careless bastard who had lived in the room.

When Boots went to the bed and turned down the covers, the landlady sniffed. "You don't have to do that, young man. Do I look like a woman that would live in a house with bedbugs?"

"No, ma'am. I'm sorry if I hurt your feelings. But I've lived in this neighborhood long enough to learn you can't be too careful. I'm sure you know that better than me. You wouldn't rent to every Tom, Dick and Harry that comes along, now, would you?"

"Well, now that you've seen it, the rate is four dollars a week in advance."

"We'll take it," I said. I peeled four aces off my small bankroll, gave them to her and asked for a receipt.

She took the money, counted it, tucked it in her bosom and said, "I don't give receipts, I know who pays and who don't. One of you better come down and get the keys."

When I thanked her for the keys she said, "You don't have to thank me. Be good boys and don't cause trouble. That's the thanks I like. You can have a drink in your room, but I don't tolerate drunkenness. If there's anything else you want to know, ask me now. I keep pretty much to myself and don't like to be disturbed."

On the way to the flophouse I handed Boots a set of keys and said, "We may as well share the place—it doesn't cost any more. When you get your gear let's buy a few groceries and I'll rustle up a feed. I'm good with a frying pan and stew pot. How about you?"

"Me? Cook? I couldn't boil a turnip. But I'm a good man with a dishrag and broom. I'd give you a deuce on the rent, but it's going to take every dime I got to piece off those foremen for the next couple of days. I'll hit you with it when we get paid from the city."

"Forget it. Your caper this morning makes you aces with me. What's a couple of bucks? It's neither here nor there if it's a right guy on the receiving end."

We bought cautiously, mostly staples, but left the store with our arms full. "I can't wait to get those pork chops in the pan and sink my teeth in a biscuit hot from the oven," I said.

"God almighty! You gonna make biscuits? I ain't ate a hot biscuit since Christ was a kid. I'd almost forgot there was such a thing. Back in St. Louis my mom never sat us down to the table without hot biscuits on it. You're making my mouth water."

"Better wait until you taste them," I cautioned, though biscuits and hotcakes were my specialty. "I haven't made a biscuit for over six months. They may not turn out very good."

We were slogging down the sidewalk, and Boots looked up. "I'm more worried about the goddamn weather than the biscuits. I think it's warming up. If the sun comes out and we get a quick thaw it'll throw a fuck on our plans for a quick stake."

"Yeah," I said. "While you were putting the figures on the horses I saw in the paper where the weatherman said there'd be rain early tomorrow. If he's right we'll be screwed. You'd better get down on your knees tonight and ask the Lord to control his bladder for a couple of days."

"Okay for you, Legs, if you want to joke about the Lord's teaching. But not me. I'm a Catholic, not a good one, but I still believe in God."

We had reached the room. I unlocked the door and went in without answering. If he was sincere, I'd respect his sincerity. I couldn't care less what he believed.

Boots put his parcels on the table, then took his shoes off and hung his wet socks up to dry before he flaked out on the bed. I busied myself with the pots and pans. At twelve-thirty I woke him up to a feed of pork chops and hot biscuits, with potatoes and turnips on the side. I ate well, but it was a treat to watch Boots gobbling biscuit after biscuit, with his meat and vegetables swimming in brown gravy. I was on my second coffee and cigarette when he finished a second helping, pushed himself back from the table and groaned. "Jesus, Legs, I haven't put my nose into a feed bag like that since I left home. You told the God's truth when you said you could cook. I'm telling you, those biscuits were as good as my mom's. I always was a skinny bastard, but I'll be hog fat in a couple of weeks if I eat like I did today."

"Glad you enjoyed it. There's nothing makes a cook happier than a hearty eater. If the snow lasts and we make a few bucks I might hold this town down long enough to fatten you up. When the new phone books come out we can make a few bucks delivering them. I hear they pay eighty cents an hour, and a cent and a half for every old book you bring back to the truck."

After Boots did the dishes we went to a pool room at Morgan and Madison and shot pool until it was time to report. On the way to the job, Boots took me down an alley behind some vacant buildings. In a deserted store a guy was selling denatured alcohol out of a bushel basket for thirty-five cents a pint. Boots picked up a pint, stuffed it under his jacket and paid the guy.

The trucks of the other foreman we'd pieced off drove in before Carter's. We stayed beside the small foreman's office and watched his crew clamber from the trucks with their shovels, then go to the tool crib and check them in. The foreman followed with four shovels on his shoulder, checked them in and brought the tags to the office. We retrieved them, waited until Carter's two trucks came back, then got our tags from him. Boots didn't give Carter the bottle of derail, and I asked him why he hadn't. "Because it's safer to give it to him with the shovels," he said.

The weatherman was right. The rain came shortly after noon the next day. But it wasn't a bad go. We got in four double shifts without lifting a single shovelful of snow.

Things had gone so well since I hit Chicago I'd discarded all thought of going south. The windfall I'd tripped over during the storm was gone, and my harvest stake was dwindling. But what the hell; I had a warm room and was scoffing regular. Boots kept his end up by clipping the pinaroos in several bowling alleys. Many of the pinboys had no home and flopped on the floor at the rear of the lanes. It seemed they slept better with an empty pocket because, as soon as the boss turned the key in the door, they shot crap until they hit tap city. Then they flattened out to catch some shut-eye.

Boots wasn't dice-smart. But he had a partner—a big gangly guy named Kelly—who was. Kelly couldn't play in the games, but Boots, an ex-pinboy, could. That's why Kelly gave him a piece of the action. They couldn't come up big because there wasn't much cash in the game. And if they tipped their duke they'd be finished for good. So Kelly played it cool and only ground out enough dough to keep him and Boots in scoff dough and walking-around money.

We spent the morning in the sack because we never hit the pad until four in the morning. After we got up and had a good meal we went our separate ways. Boots went to Drell's, a gambling joint that ran a book. He never bucked the games, but he made numerous small bets on the nags. If he hit a lick one day he blew it the next, but he never lost hope. He was sure it was only a matter of time till he'd make a killing. I tried to beat a Kelly game in the pool room at Morgan and Madison until seven o'clock. Then Boots would come in and we'd go to supper. By eight-thirty I'd have a stick in my hand again and play until the joint closed for the night. Then I'd buy a paper and go to Thomson's, a one-armed cafeteria, where I'd read the news over a coffee until Boots showed up. Then, after a final coffee, we'd go home.

The second week of the new year, when I was down to my last sawbuck, I got a break. I had stopped playing Kelly, because most shooters that played every day were as good as I was or better. And there was no percentage in risking my last ten-spot in a game where, at best, the odds were even. There's a saying among smart money boys: "A guy with the shorts can never get well taking an even break for his case dough."

I still went to the pool room every day to play house pool and hustled the odd buck whenever I was lucky enough to meet a mooch willing to play for small stakes. One afternoon I had no one to play with and was watching the Kelly game. Nick, the house man, brought a fuddy-duddy over and asked me to play him a few games of pool.

I gave the guy my duke and said, "My name's Legs. What kind of game you want to play?"

He gripped my hand and said, with a strong German accent, "Boston is good. Kurt Von Mohenfels my name."

The handle fit him to a tee. He was an oddball and looked the part, but he turned out to be good people in spite of it. His head (except his thick black eyebrows that ran together like a hedge) had no more hair on it than the cue ball. He moved slowly and deliberately as if he had all the time in the world, and it was something to watch him puffing on a stogie. He held it the way a Hoosier who never smoked anything but a corncob smokes a cigarette. You know the way I mean: the cigar between the first and second fingers close to the palm. When he put the cigar in his kisser he covered it with his hand.

You may gather from my remarks that Herr Mohenfels was a yokel. Not so. He was a lonely man, but very smart. Until his wife died three months before, he'd had only two interests: Bertha, his bride, and his tool-and-die shop on Lake Street.

After Bertha's death he sold his north-end home and built an apartment over his shop. Loneliness had taken him to the pool room. When I learned this, I tried to make his hours around the table pleasant and relaxing. We played for fifteen-cent cigars, and I'd grind nine or ten out of him every night. I'm sure he knew I turned them in to Nick for cash (since I didn't smoke them), but he never let on. He also knew I wasn't working and needed the money.

But everything went down the crapper about three o'clock one morning when Boots and I were heading home. We saw a rubby passed out in a doorway, a half-bottle of rubbing alcohol lying on his chest. Normally we would have gone past without a second thought, but it was so goddamn cold I knew he'd freeze to death.

"We better get him up and walk him or he'll die," I said.

"Screw it," said Boots. "He's so goddamn full of anti-freeze he wouldn't ice up at the North Pole. If a cop spots us rousting him, he'll swear we're jackrolling and run us in. The guy's a lush. Let him lie there. The Lord looks after them."

But I couldn't. I had just bent over to shake the rubby awake when the squad car turned onto Madison and hit us with its spotlight. To have let go of the rubby then would have fingered us as jackrollers so I kept trying to roust him until the big Cadillac pulled up to the curb.

Four large bruisers bounded out of the car simultaneously and surrounded us. One big fuzz grabbed me by the shoulders, yanked me up and barked, "What the hell are you punks doing with that drunk?"

"We're trying to wake the old fellow up and get him on his feet," I said.

"What the hell you doing that for? I'm goddamn sure neither of you ever saw him before. So you better have a damn good reason for being in this doorway rousting a drunk at four o'clock in the morning."

"The only reason, and I don't think there's a better one, is if someone doesn't get him on his feet and out of here he'll freeze to death. But now that you're here, he's your baby," I said, and started to leave. The big cop stepped in front of me and gave me a shot with his belly that jarred me into his cohorts. "Not so fast, wise guy. You're not going anywhere. You say you're worried about the rummy freezing to death. A hell of a lot you or anyone else could care what happens to him. The world won't lose a goddamn thing if he did. He's not living. Any son of a bitch that drinks that stuff is dead already. You know, and I know, the only thing you two bums care about is his wallet."

The cops closed us in, and before I could answer another of the big bastards took the play away from him. He grabbed me with his big pussy glommers, picked me up like I was a five-year-old and dangled me in the air, shaking me so that my head bobbed around like a buoy in a gale. Then he slammed me down so hard a sharp pain tore up my legs all the way to my chin when my feet hit the cement.

"What's your name?" he bellowed.

I gave him a phony.

"Where do you work?"

"Ward's Bakery." It was a nearby plant.

"Let's see your hands."

I turned them palms up and held them out to his kisser, knowing he was looking for calluses and would find none. But by now rage had shifted the gears of my noggin into high, and I had the answer for what I knew he was going to hit me with.

The smirk on his kisser heightened. "From the look of your hands you haven't worked for months," he jeered. "They're as soft as a schoolmarm's. You'll need a better answer than that."

I put a little air between the big shitheel and myself before I said, "You don't get calluses from greasing pans."

When the other cops snickered they hurt my case. No young punk was going to make him look stupid in front of his fellow officers and get off scot free. I studied his face in the streetlight and saw his jaw tighten and his face get redder than the glow of the light on the corner.

"Okay, wise guy, who do you work for there? What's the name of your boss?" he snarled.

Without hesitation I gave him the first name that came to my mind. "Donnelly. A big fellow by the name of Donnelly."

"Donnelly, Donnelly? I thought Jim Pears was the boss there," he said.

That threw me, but not for long. Jesus Christ, I thought, this bastard's got me, and it's the Bridewell for sure. All the tales I'd heard about Cook County Jail flashed through my mind. Then it hit me. The son of a bitch was bluffing. He didn't know any more about Ward's Bakery than I did.

"Jim Pears?" I said. "I never heard of any Jim Pears around there. Morley Donnelly's the boss." I guessed right, and I had him cold.

"Where do you live?"

No sweat there. I had an honest answer. "We live at 1342 Washington."

"Get in the car. We'll soon find out if you're lying or not."

We got in the car, Boots and me in the back seat with the mouthy cop, and they took us home.

"All right, you guys, there's the house. I'm giving you a break. If you really live here you got a key to get in, but if you don't have a key, you better crap one or you'll be in the show-up tomorrow. You might get through the lineup without being fingered, but that won't stop you getting thirty days in Bridewell making bricks for the county."

We were almost to the house when the big prick doing the talking bellowed, "Come here," loud enough to wake everyone in the neighborhood. We retraced our steps to the car, and he stuck his head out the window along with his right arm, which he waved for emphasis.

"You may think you're getting away with something if you live here. But mark this down in your little black book. I'm in charge of this squad, and I've just been moved into this precinct. This car is on the prowl in this neighborhood every night. So if I see either of you punks on the street after midnight I'll lock you up and have the judge throw away the key. Now get in the house if you can."

When he unlocked the door, Boots mumbled something about the fuzz waiting at the curb. "What the hell you mumbling about? Don't tell me you got bull horrors?" I joked.

"I wasn't mumbling, and I ain't got no bull horrors. I've had too many run-ins with them for that. What I said was, it's no goddamn wonder everyone hates their guts. I don't mind telling you, that bastard put the shit up my neck. But I'll say this: you sure came up big when that asshole asked you where you worked. How the hell did you know there was no boss at Ward's by the name of Jim Pears?"

"I'm not a gambler like you, but once in a while I play a long shot. I figured the cop was bluffing, so I bet all my chips on snake-eyes."

We didn't switch the hall light on. We watched the cops through the door's glass panel until they took off. Then we made it to the room before either of us spoke. Boots flipped the light on, then flopped on the bed and said, "That copper means business. He's got our number now. Maybe we'd be smart to blow town for a while."

"Yeah, I suppose we should, but goddamn it, we're getting by pretty good, me with Mohenfels and you with Kelly. Why not sleep on it? If we watch our step, there's a good chance we can keep out of the big dick's way."

"The only sure way to keep out of it is to leave town. I sure called the shot on that goddamn rubby. I wonder if the cops got a walking bull to look after him?"

"I hope they did," I said, as I turned the fire on under the kettle. "Let's have a coffee while we sort it out."

"I'm for that, because I won't get to sleep till we do."

Waiting for the coffee to perk I rolled a butt and tossed the makings on the bed to Boots. He sat up, rolled one for himself and when he licked the paper, said, "I think I'll go home and eat the old folks' spuds till spring. I can grab the head end of a C. and A. passenger out of Cicero tomorrow night and be in St. Louis in the morning."

"If we do that we'll blow the two weeks' rent we paid today," I said.

"Then you'll come? You could hole up with the folks till you got squared away."

"No," I said. "I'm thinking of California and tree-ripened oranges. I'd hole up there a month before going to Montana for the lambing season."

"I been wanting to go home for two years, but I wouldn't because I couldn't go top-drawer. Now I'm pissing my pants to get there."

"Hold it! I never said I'd go, but if your going home hinges on whether I go or not, I'll go—because you should go home."

"Christ, Legs, you make me feel like a guy that don't care about his family. I love them all, but I couldn't go home with the ass out of my pants."

"Okay, we'll go. But I'm going to bat it through to the coast. I don't know what you're holding, but I'm only packing eighty cents. So I'll hit the stem long enough to get a three- or four-buck road stake. And you raise what you can."

When we got out of the sheets Boots ate a good meal. But I only had a coffee, because it's not good to go begging on a full gut if you're trying to lay up a few bucks. Many generous jokers will feed a bum—give him a run-in—but won't trust him with the price of a meal. They think—sometimes with reason—that if they give cash the bum will fan his ass to the nearest bootlegger for a pint of rotgut. And it makes it tough on a bum trying to get a few bucks together if one or two men you ding give you a run-in.

I did well on the street, but got back-to-back run-ins, and my stomach felt and looked like a cow's the day before she drops her calf. I'd picked up a little over two dollars in hard when I sidled up to a big bruiser staring in a store window and said, "Pardon me, friend. Could you help a hungry man out with the price of a bite to eat?"

When he turned and faced me I knew I'd begged a copper. My only hope was to Hoosier up and make him think I was a green punk that didn't know the score.

"Aren't you afraid of making the band house?" he asked.

"Band house, what's that?" I stammered.

"Jail, that's what the band house is."

"Jail!" I said. "What for?"

"Don't you know it's against the law to stem people on the street?"

"Stemming? What's stemming? I don't know what you mean."

His face got red and he said, "Young man, I don't know whether you're Hoosiering up on me or not. I'd hate to think you are, because I don't like to be taken in. It doesn't pay in my work. So you better be leveling with me."

"I'm not sure what you mean by Hoosiering, sir, but I'm not doing anything but being honest. I haven't had anything to eat since noon yesterday," I parried.

"Okay, son, I'll give you the benefit of the doubt and say you're leveling with me. Come with me," he commanded, and crossed the street.

I turned to follow and saw the squad car across the street in front of a café. Oh-oh! I thought, there'll be no St. Louis for me. It'll be the Bridewell instead. But my hole card was still face down, and I didn't turn it up until we crossed the street. When the cop went to the squad car I ignored the big black Cadillac and was opening the café door when he called out, "Where the hell you going?"

"In the restaurant—isn't that where you're taking me?"

"Jesus, kid! You're either goddamn green or goddamn clever. I told you I'd give you the benefit of the doubt and I still will, because I don't think it's possible for a punk to be that road smart."

Then he turned to the other cops: "This kid's something else. I can't put the figures on him, but he seems to be on the level. If he's lying, then he's too smart to tip his hand answering questions on the street, and if he isn't it would be a shame to take him in."

Then he reached in his pocket, pulled out his change and said to the other coppers, "Come on you guys, hit me with your small change for the kid."

I can't say whether he was in charge or not, but the other cops cleaned their pockets of hard and handed it to him.

When he gave me the money, he said, "Here, kid, this ought to keep you eating for a couple of days. I don't know where you're from or how you got here, and you don't have to tell me. But take my advice and go home before you get in trouble. If you ever find your way to the skid row and the wolves get a-hold of you, you're a goner. Just remember when you get home that cops aren't always the bad guys people think they are." I thanked him profusely, then hurried into the café where I sat on a stool near the window and watched with relief as the car drove off.

I had the money spread out on the counter and was counting it when the counterman came over. It totaled two dollars and eighty cents, and when I scooped it up to put in my kick with the other money I'd stemmed, the guy said, "That's a lot of silver. Looks like you been in a penny-ante poker game and the cards broke your way."

"You guessed it," I said, as I pocketed the coins. "All I want is a coffee with a little extra sugar."

Thinking the squad car might circle the block to make sure I was stowing chow away I kept my peepers glued to the window, sipped coffee slowly and inhaled deep drags of smoke to stem my queasiness. I dallied long enough for the car to have circled the block several times. When it didn't, the waves of anxiety began to abate and I became bold enough to give the stem another whirl. But in case I pulled another rock and the next cop gave me a fast frisk, I exchanged the hard money for soft, rolled four ace notes tightly and buried them in the tobacco bag.

The buck and a half of hard I'd stashed in my boots had me limping by the time I got back to skid row.

It was after seven when I got back to the room, and I was making a lump for the road when Boots came in.

"Don't make any sandwiches for me. I already ate," he said.

"So have I, but I thought they'd go pretty good about the time we hit Springfield. It doesn't seem right to leave all this grub here."

"How did you make out on the stem? I was lucky. I caught up with Kelly at Drell's. He was thirty bucks up at the time and in a generous mood. 'Deuce, hell,' he told me, 'here's a fin,' and he tossed me a blue chip. That gave me time to check on the train. It leaves Cicero on the nose at ten."

"Good. I did a little better. But I had a run-in with the law. I'll tell you about it on the train. There's a paper on the chair by the table if you want to look at tomorrow's entries while I finish these sandwiches. We better leave about eight-thirty if we want to hit the yards in time to check them out."

Before we left I went to the landlady's rooms and told her we were leaving. She thanked me for telling her but never came up with a refund—and I didn't ask for one. To my way of thinking she was making up for a few of the many times she'd been beaten out of a week's rent by fly-by-nights before she got smart enough to collect in advance.

CHAPTER 13

WHEN WE STARTED FOR THE RAILWAY YARD THE night was clear and still. The full amber moon and millions of stars shone from an ebony background. But by the time we got there the temperature had dropped and a light snow was falling.

There was a string of heated day coaches on a side track not far from the station. We climbed inside one and waited until we heard the highball, then hurried outside and stood in the shelter of the car until the big road hog appeared.

"Come on, let's board her," I shouted as the engine loomed out of the darkness. I intended to climb aboard the rear of the engine's water tender.

Boots grabbed my arm and said, "Not yet. I've rode this train before. It always has four or five mail coaches, and it's warmer riding in the space between them, called a blind. Let's wait for the fourth blind, because the farther we get from the engine the less cinders we'll eat."

By then, the first and only mail car on the train went by and the steps of the first day coach showed up. Although we legged it as fast as we could to get to the front end of the mail car and grab the blind between it and the tender, we were losing ground.

"Screw this!" I screamed, fighting to make myself heard over the train's din. "Grab the steps of the coach. We'll ride them to the first stop." And I clambered aboard with Boots on my tail.

After we'd made ourselves as comfortable as we could, Boots took out his makings, shook some tobacco in a paper, stuck the ends of the tie-strings in his teeth and gave the bag a tug to close it. Then he handed it to me. "All the comforts of home," he grinned.

"Could be a little warmer and a little less breezy," I said, after licking and sealing the paper.

We were sitting on the steps puffing away when the coach door opened. The brakeman had come to drop the platform, which was hinged to the end of the baggage car above the steps. When lowered it becomes a platform between the cars. We hadn't counted on his lowering the platform.

"Where the hell do youse two think you're going?" he asked, but not unkindly.

"Kansas City," I said.

"Maybe so, but not here. What the hell you doing on these steps? Why aren't you up front on the blind where you should be? Jesus Christ, is this the first time youse of ever beat your way?"

I was going to tell him how we'd missed the blind, but instead I decided to go the Hoosier route.

"That's right, sir. We've never rode a train without a ticket before. But we had to get to Kansas City and we don't have any money. Couldn't you just put the platform down and let us ride to the first stop? Then we'll get on the engine."

"First stop? Hell, man, this train don't stop until we get to Joliet, and that's forty miles. When I put this platform down you'll be sitting in a sixty-mile-an-hour down-draft. You'll be froze to death by the time we get there. I'll have to tell the conductor. It's his baby. He's the one who has to figure out what's to be done with youse guys. No need to tell you to stay here; you can't go anywhere." Then he left.

"Holy Christ!" said Boots. "If it isn't one thing it's another. I knew things were going too good to last. We've stepped in a bear trap, and when the law gets through with us we'll be caged up for sixty days—unless you can handle the conductor better than I can."

"I sure as hell intend to try," I said. "But it'll depend on what kinda guy he is. If he's a right guy we still have a chance to get out of this mess your bright idea got us into. But if he's a prick we're dead. It's the county jail for sure. We'll have to play it by ear, and I think it's better to let one guy do the talking. That way we're not so apt to get our story fucked up. If you like I'll carry the ball."

"Go ahead. You're a better con artist than me. But what the hell you going to tell him?"

"I don't know. I'll wait until he opens up, then think of something. If the worst happens the county will put a roof over our heads and feed us till spring. Then I won't have to go to California. It's only a few miles to Kansas, and by the time we're out they'll be putting the crop in. I'll head there and work for a scissor bill till his seeding's done."

"How can you make a joke out outta getting locked up? We should have our asses kicked for grabbing this goddamn coach."

"I'll buy that," I said. "But whose idea was it not to catch the first blind?"

The bickering was still going on when the conductor came through the doorway and stood glowering at us for at least thirty seconds with his hands on his hips. Then he shook his head in disgust and growled, "Get off your butts and come inside."

We followed him into the coach where he motioned us to sit on two empty seats beside the door. Then he sat in the opposite seat, shook his head and said, "I been on this road since I was a kid, and that's over forty years. With a record that long I've seen a lot of hobos and seen them do weird things. But this tops them all. What the hell made you think you could get away with beating a ride on a passenger coach? If you got away with this, the next time you climbed on a train you'd probably board a Pullman, and if you got away with that, you'd want a lower berth. Now sit here while I make my rounds and decide what to do with the pair of you."

After he walked down the aisle, Boots said, "He seems like a pretty good egg. What do you think he'll do? Have you figured out what kind of a line you're going to give him?"

"Not yet, but I'm working on it. One thing for sure, I got to come up with something good. He doesn't strike me as a man that will swallow any bullshit. But you can be goddamn sure of one thing. He's not going to risk forty years on the line for a couple of ding hiesers like us. He's not that stupid."

While I was talking Boots turned and took a gander down the car. "We've just ran out of time. He's almost here. I hope you're ready for him."

"Ready as I'll ever be," I said without confidence.

The conductor sat down and silently eyed us until we began to squirm. Finally he said, "I'm not a hard man, but my years on the railroad have taught me a lot about people. Thirty years ago you lads wouldn't have been a problem. Now it's different. I try to see other people's side of the coin. I don't want to turn you in, but what the hell else can I do? I've worked for the road all my life. In six years they'll put me out to pasture with a damn good pension. No man's going to give that up unless he's stupid. You look like you're both bright enough to understand that. How come you did such a stupid thing?"

His words and his cool approach made our plight look hopeful. It was good to see he was a man who didn't panic. But because of this I would have to take another tack.

"You're right," I said. "It was stupid. I'm not going to try and shit you, because I know you're smart enough to read me." I respected what he said too much to let that happen, I said. "Also, I respect your white hair because my mother always taught me to respect white-headed people. She said, 'White hair is a sign of wisdom and tolerance. It shows a person has lived long enough to learn many things, and wisdom stems from knowledge.' She's gone now," I went on, "but I still try to follow her teaching. I could tell you this is the first train I ever caught, but you'd know it was a lie."

The short dapper conductor smiled and tipped his cap, exposing a wrinkled brow. He was about to speak when I cut him off.

"We've both hopped lots of trains and shoulda known better, but it's done now. We were going to catch the fourth or fifth blind, but there was only one mail car on the train, and when it went by it was grab the steps of the coach or miss the train. From what you say I know you want to do what's right. You could, as you said, turn us over to the law. But that would bother you for a while, and you'd rather do it another way if you could.

"Let me say this, and it's the truth. If you got fired and lost your pension, I'd rather go to jail than see it happen.

"But there's another way out of this mess, one that could give everyone peace of mind. We're not hand-cuffed to the seat, and there's no one but you to stop us from lifting the platform and jumping off the train as we pull into Joliet. Then, when you get off the train you can report us—but we'll be long gone."

While I was talking I studied him closely, and twice I saw a look of compassion cross his face: once when I mentioned my mother's teaching, and again when I spoke of going to jail. He was such a good listener I could have kept right on talking. But instinct told me to clam up.

He tipped his cap back on his head, and stroked his chin with his thumb and first finger for a while. Then he said, "I thought about that, and I know it might work. But I have to think about the people I work for. I know what I should do. I also know what I want to do. I'll tell you what: you sit tight. It will be thirty minutes before we get to Joliet, and I want to put some more thought on it. I'll let you know what I decide before we arrive."

When the conductor left, Boots took the seat he had vacated and had a good view of everyone in the coach.

"Know what, Legs? Every goddamned yokel in the car's pissing his pants wondering what's going on. I'll lay ten to one some nosy bastard will be up here in five minutes putting the quiz on us."

"Let them come. I'll put the rigging on every Joe that shows."

"Hey, man! Here they come now. Two of them. How's that for handicapping? I should open a bookie joint."

They arrived: a tall pimple-faced man in his mid-thirties and a squat broad-shouldered character in a ten-gallon hat, wearing large horn-rimmed googs with thick lenses. With a voice loud enough to reach to the end of the coach, Pimples asked, "Are you boys in trouble with the conductor?"

"Well, you could call it that," I said. "It's as good a word as any for it. Sit down, sir, and I'll fill you in."

They sat, and I went on: "Names don't mean much here, but mine's I. P. Freely. My friends call me I. P., and this is Jim McHann. His friends call him Boots."

"Glad to meet you," said Googs, without offering his hand or giving us their monikers. "The trouble," I said, "really started last week. Boots and I were pearl diving in a café in Chicago. That's dishwashing, if it doesn't ring a bell."

"What kind of trouble?" interrupted Pimples. "Did it have anything to do with the police?"

"No, not then, but it may before long." I was leading them slow, trying to give them a good build-up. "The job in the café wasn't much for pay. All we made was five dollars a week and our meals. The room took most of that, and you always have to buy a few things, you know, like smokes, newspapers, a pair of socks or some little thing like toothpaste or shaving cream. We never had money for shows or nothing like that."

"Yeah, yeah, but what was the trouble?" Googs was getting impatient.

"I'm coming to that, but it takes time. I got to tell it like it is. Boots got this letter from his father. That's the first time Boots ever got a letter from his pa, and it scared him, and rightly so. You see, his father wrote cause his mother couldn't. She was too sick to write. His pa begged him to come home, but Boots couldn't go because he didn't have any money to pay his fare. Then last night Boots got a wire saying his mother was going to die but wanted to see Boots before she passed away."

"Yeah, but what's this got to do with the police?" asked Pimples.

"Well, at that time it didn't. But Boots had to get home, and the only way he could was to sneak a ride on a train. He was afraid to go alone, so I said I'd go with him. That's where the police come in. You see, we didn't know how to go about it, and we caught a ride on the steps of a coach. That's where the brakeman found us, and the conductor brought us in here. He's going to turn us over to the police when we get to Joliet. He said not to worry, the judge is a good man, never gave a hobo more than sixty days for train riding. That means Boots will be in jail instead of at his mother's bedside when she passes on. If he had brought his father's letter with him he could show you where it was his mother's last wish to see him. Now he won't even be able to attend her funeral."

"That's a damn shame," murmured Googs, "I wish there was something we could do to help." He took off his Stetson and swabbed the sweatband with his handkerchief.

"Yeah, I wish there was," echoed Pimples.

They were set up for the double-play. I scooped up the ball and fired it back. "You can help, and thanks for the offer. It's funny how it works, but it always does. They say the Lord has ways of providing, and he does it in funny ways. He sent you men, I'm sure. If we can scrape up the fare from Chicago to Joliet we've got it made. The conductor won't be able to turn us over to the police, and I'm sure, now that God's got us out of this mess, he'll find a way to get us the rest of the way."

"How much is the fare?" stammered Pimples.

"I'm not sure. It can't be very much; it isn't very far. Three dollars apiece should be enough to cover it."

"Three dollars each? That's six dollars! We couldn't give you that kind of money." Pimples squirmed.

I said, "Yes, I guess it is asking a lot. But maybe, between the two of you, you could give us a couple of dollars? We might be able to get the rest from some of the other passengers. I'm sure if they knew the kind of fix we were in they'd be glad to help. Even if it happened we couldn't get more, the money would buy us tobacco, toothpaste and razor blades in jail."

"Well, I guess a dollar apiece won't break us," said Stetson. "We'd like to give you what you need, but we're a little short ourselves. We're coming from a convention in Chicago where we spent more time in speakeasies than we did at the convention—and that runs away with a lot of dough." He fumbled in his pocket, pulled out a small roll of bills, peeled off two aces and handed them to me. "That'll look after my pal, too. He went broke in a crap game in a Chicago hotel room."

"Thank you very kindly. May God be good to you for this kind act," I said.

While I was telling the story Boots sat in silence, trying, and managing quite convincingly, to look like a grief-stricken mourner. Most of the time he kept his head lowered and his palms together between his knees, as if he was sneaking a word with God, looking up now and again with the sad watery eyes of a dying calf.

I deliberately spoke loud enough to reach as many ears as possible. I knew by the hush in our end of the car that everyone within sound of my voice was on the eary. People, especially Americans, have big hearts for anyone in distress. They readily open their pocketbooks to help if the appeal has a little drama attached to it.

When they made their offering and returned to their seats, Boots whispered, "You son of a bitch, Legs, I gotta hand it to you. You sure came up with a good begging line. I had a hard time to keep a straight face."

"Straight face, my ass," I said, keeping my voice down. "You should go on the stage. You looked as wilted as a prune in a basket of ripe plums."

"Don't look round, Legs. I'll keep you posted. I think the two guys that were sitting behind us are taking up a collection. They got up and followed the guy with the ten-gallon hat and his pal down the aisle, and they're talking to four other guys now. Now the guys they were talking to are digging in their kicks. Could be I'm wrong, but from here it looks good. Yeah, they're all shelling out. I hope it's for us and not a payoff on a bet. Hang tight, here they come with a fist full of soft. For Christ's sake, don't look round." Boots covered his excitement with a long face for the benefit of the two guys coming up the aisle.

Before they reached us Boots bent over and made out like he was tying his shoe laces. And I said nonchalantly, "What's the matter with those laces? You can't keep them tied."

"I don't know. I never had trouble with the old pair." Then, timing it on the nose, he straightened up, looking grief-stricken, and said in a dismal voice, "Hello. Do you want to sit with us?" and he moved over and made room.

In contrast to the gloomy look on Boots' kisser, the faces of the two men in the aisle reflected the feeling of joy in their hearts. Looking at their beaming kissers it struck me that there's no satisfaction that compares with the joy of giving. Our ruse had served two purposes: it gave us some ready cash and provided gratification to the givers.

"I hope you don't think we were eavesdropping," said the taller of the two natty men. "We couldn't help overhearing what you told those two fellows, and we'd like to help. We're with four other friends on the train. We've been taking in the six-day bike races at the Chicago Colosseum and still have a few dollars we didn't spend.

Joe here and I got the other guys to ante a dollar each and came up with a buck ourselves. We'd like to give it to you to help with the fare."

When he finished talking he gave me the money. Boots spoke for the second time since we entered the coach. In a melancholy voice he said, "I can't thank you enough because I don't have the words. I just hope my mother's alive when I get home. I'd like to tell her about the kind people we met on the train." And I'll be goddamned if I know how he did it, but he dropped a few tears as he spoke.

The performance Boots put on embarrassed our benefactors so much they told us we were more than welcome, then took off down the aisle to where their buddies were sitting.

According to my figures we were only about five minutes out of Joliet and every turn of the wheels brought us closer—and still no conductor. This put us in another sweat. We reasoned he had gone for the train company instead of us and was putting off the bad news until we hit the outskirts of Joliet. That way he lessened the chance of our creating a scene or his having to hold us by force.

We'd given up hope of getting a break, when the trainman came into the coach and started to open some of the small windows near the ceiling with a hook on a long wooden rod. When he got to where we were he stopped and hooked the window down.

"I'm going to lift the platform when I finish here. How you handle it after that is your affair. Don't ride her into the station or you're goners. Don't bother to thank me. Good luck." He gave the window a final tug and left.

We stayed in our seat after the trainman left until we heard the eerie moan of the big locomotive's whistle. Then we hurried outside and waited for the train's speed to slacken. Boots was standing on the bottom step gripping the handrail, and I urged him to hit the ground.

"Jesus Christ, Legs," he yelled, "not yet! There's gotta be at least ten inches of snow on the right of way. I can't run fast enough in it, and you know as well as me what'll happen if I don't."

"You're damn right I know. But would you rather have a roll in the snow or a stretch in the can? If you're not going, I am. So get the hell out of the way and let me go first."

That did it. Boots hit the snow clutching the handrail with both hands, but the train was going so fast and the snow was so deep his feet couldn't obey his bidding and he had to let go of the handrail. I saw him go down and figured he was a goner when he came bouncing into view beside the train. I stood and watched as he bounded like a high hopper for thirty more yards before he stopped. From the train the huddled heap looked like a bundle of rags that had fallen off a junk wagon.

Watching Boots only took a few seconds, but I had no time left and I jumped too. When I hit the ground the train had slowed a little since Boots did his tumbling act. I took about three giant strides, then it felt like my arms were being pulled from their sockets. I let go. When I did, I took off through the air like an arrow from a longbow. After a flight of twenty feet I landed head first in the snow.

I scrambled to my feet unhurt, but minus my cap. The snow, the villain when I unloaded, befriended me on landing—acting as a buffer above the gravel roadbed. I was so concerned about Boots I didn't stop to look for my cap or brush myself off, but legged it back to where I'd seen him huddled beside the tracks.

It scared the shit out of me when I spotted him crawling around on his hands and knees in the snow. I thought he'd been hit and screamed, "What the hell happened? Did you bust a leg or something?"

"Hell, no! I'm okay. I lost a shoe and I'm looking for it."

"Christ, you scared me," I said. "Maybe you lost it when you hit the ground. I'll look farther back. I lost my cap, too, but I'll look for it later. Shit, man! You sure got a talent. You should of seen the tumbling act you put on after you let go of the handrail. Coming out of that with no broken bones, you could be a stunt man. Maybe you should go to California with me and give it a shot."

"Go on, make jokes, you long-legged bastard. But when I was bouncing down the track I was scared shitless. I was afraid I'd hit a switch. I once saw a guy get his jumping off a train that was going too fast. He took about three big steps before he flew through the air and came down on one of those short switches and it went right through him. So have your joke if you think it's funny, but don't expect me to laugh too."

"Come on, Boots, I had my problems too. We're lucky neither of us got hurt. You stay here, and I'll go look around at your port of entry for your shoe.

I found the shoe close to where Boots had made his leap. When I returned with it his mood took an upturn. He put it on, and we walked up the track, found my cap and headed for the main drag to put the nose bag on and get a flop for the night.

CHAPTER 14

JOLIET, LOCATED ON THE DESPLANES RIVER AND SET
amid rich farmlands, was an industrial and railroad center. It was
also the site of the Illinois state penitentiary.

When we entered the city, the streets were dark except for an
occasional light in a window and dim street lamps that lit concrete-
block warehouses and made eerie shadows on the snow. We walked
four blocks in this dreary section without a sign of life when Boots,
whose feet were freezing, suddenly snapped, "What a fucking
town! Where the hell are all the natives? Even the fucking law's
deserted the goddamn place."

"Don't be too sure about the cops," I said. "They're around.
Right now they're probably holed up someplace guzzling free coffee
and doughnuts. As for the natives, where the hell would you be on
a night like this? Not plowing through a snowstorm at this hour.
You'd be in the fur with your wife or girlfriend. That's where you'd
be. But I think you're coming out with a seven or eleven. The dice
are getting hot. The light on the next corner looks bigger than the
candles they got along the street."

I was right. At the next corner, the street crossed the lower end
of the main gut. Here the lighted windows of the stores added their
candle power to the closer-spaced street lamps—but still no natives.
In the middle of the block we came to a high-class eatery, with three
guys and a broad sitting at a table near the window. We went in and
stood in front of the small cash-register counter until a Greek came
over. When he found out all we wanted was directions to a cheap
flophouse he looked relieved. I'm sure he thought we were going to
heist the joint, or put the beg on him for a meal.

He called to the people at the table and asked if they knew any
cheap rooming houses. One of them came over and told us to go
three blocks farther up the main drag, then turn right for two
blocks. We couldn't miss, he said. Every house from there on took
in roomers. That wasn't the kind of flop we were looking for, but we
thanked him and left no wiser than before.

We kept walking the stem until we came to a greasy spoon and went in. It was a one-man operation: a horseshoe counter that sat about twenty people, no tables or booths. The only furniture was a big, old-fashioned, walk-in icebox against the wall between the two swinging doors at the rear. The room was empty when we peered through the dirty plate-glass window, and we thought the place was closed. But we saw lights in the kitchen between the swinging doors. We tried the door on the chance the night man was working in the kitchen. It was open, so we went and sat on counter stools. Seconds later, a good-looking guy in a white apron came through the swinging doors with a stepladder and stood it against the icebox.

"Be with you in a minute," he said, as he climbed the ladder.

When his head reached the top of the icebox, he reached under his apron and pulled a .22 caliber pistol from his belt, climbed up two rungs and steadied the arm with the gun on top of the icebox. Then he sighted along the barrel and waited.

We sat watching and wondering what the hell he was up to and whether to get the hell out of there before we found out.

"What do you think the crazy bastard's gonna do with that rod?" Boots whispered. "You think the sonabitch is crazy enough to fire it in here? Let's get the fuck out while the getting's good."

"Just a minute," I said. "Let's see it out. I don't know what he's aiming at, but it ain't us, so don't get yourself all lathered up. I couldn't sleep if I didn't find out what the crazy bastard's gonna shoot."

But I wanted to get the hell out as much as Boots, and I would have if the guy hadn't pulled the trigger. The gun must have been loaded with .22 long shells, because the report was deafening. And the gun's recoil jerked the guy's arm off the icebox. But then he stuffed the gat in his belt, reached across and climbed down holding a dead rat by the tail.

"I'll be with you soon as I get rid of this little bastard," he said, grinning, as he headed through the kitchen door—presumably to the alley behind, because we felt the blast of cold air.

"Christ," said Boots. "He probably won't even wash his hands when he's finished. I don't know about you, but I sure as hell ain't eating anything here. Let's get the hell out before he comes back."

"Okay," I said, "but let's grab a coffee first. Besides, we got to ask him where the skid row is. There's probably not another joint in town still open, and we don't want to spend all night looking for a flophouse."

"Yeah, you're right. I'll have a cup of coffee, but I'm not eating. Every bite would taste of dead rat."

The waiter came to the counter, drying his hands on his apron. "What'll it be, men? Can I start you off with a coffee? Wasn't that a big sonofabitch? I was cutting pork chops for tomorrow's dinner when I heard a kind of a rustle. I looked up and nearly shit myself. There was this sonofabitch squatting on his haunches, staring at me. I let fly with the cleaver, but he scooted in here and went up the side of the fridge. I grabbed the broom and waited for him to come down, but the bastard knew I was waiting and stayed there. I got the pistol from the till and stood on the counter, but couldn't see him, and then I remembered the stepladder. That's when you came in."

He laughed. "Guess you wondered what was going on, eh? I had to get that bastard. I hate rats worse than snakes. I just scoured hell out of my hands, but they still feel clammy." Then he took the towel tucked in his apron and wiped his hands again before pouring us coffee.

"We didn't really want anything," I said, "except to find out if you could tell us where the skid row was. But thanks for the coffees. They'll warm us up."

"Sure. It's about six blocks from here. Go right when you leave here, then turn left at the next corner and keep going. You'll run right into it." Then he poured himself a coffee and refilled ours. "Where you from, anyway? Must be tough riding a freight on a night like this."

"Sure is. We're from Chi. And thanks for the directions. We'll get going as soon as we finish these coffees." I added the latter because it looked like he could babble all night.

"Don't worry. They're on the house. You like a couple of sinkers to go with them? They're on the house too."

"Thanks, I sure could go for one before hitting the sack," I said.

Boots didn't answer, but when the owner brought me two doughnuts he brought him two as well, plopped them on the counter and left before we could thank him. I dunked one in the coffee, took a bite and was surprised to see Boots do the same.

"That's what I like about you, Boots. You're a man of your word. 'I wouldn't eat anything in this goddamned joint if I was starving.' "

"Yeah." He grinned sheepishly. "Go ahead, have your kicks. But when the guy told about scrubbing his hands, I knew he was okay. Don't be so goddamned smug."

I laughed. "Hey, I wonder if there's a train outta here in the morning?"

"Know what? If we have to retrace our steps six blocks before turning right, we'll be close to the station. My feet are in pretty good shape now. Why not go look on the call board and see when the next train leaves? It may be late for the natives, but it's the middle of the afternoon for a pair of night hoots like us."

"Suits me," I said, and ten minutes later we were passing the seedy buildings of the skid row. At the third or fourth flophouse, I asked Boots how his feet were doing. "They're starting to nip a little," he said, "but let's keep going to the station. Maybe the newsstand is open and I can get a racing form."

"What the hell you going to do with a racing form if you find one?" I snorted. "You think the hogger or the tallow pot will book a bet?"

"Sure. Don't you know all the guys on this line work for the syndicate?" Boots cracked. "But you're right. If there's a morning train I won't buy one."

We were farther from the station than we thought. It took us another fifteen minutes. During that time a wind came up and the temperature dropped. By the time we arrived, Boots's feet were so cold he was starting to limp. So we decided to go the station to thaw out before checking the schedule. We were nearly there when we saw two bums scurry out the door—followed by the railroad bull.

"This ain't no flophouse," he was shouting. "Find yourself some place else to sleep or I'll fix you a place to sack out for sixty days. I'm just warning you this time, but if I see you again I'll lay trespassing charges."

We stopped and watched, hoping the bull wouldn't spot us. Boots had to get inside before he froze his feet, and I was goddamn cold myself. When the copper went into the express office we ran to the station. As Boots went inside, I checked the train schedule. According to it, we'd be spending tomorrow in Joliet. When I went in to give Boots the news, he was putting his wet socks on the radiator and didn't hear me. His socks were so wet they left water marks on the floor when he walked.

"For Christ's sake, man!" I growled. "Have you been walking around with your feet that wet? You're gonna catch pneumonia."

Startled, he wheeled around. "Jesus, Legs! I thought it was the copper. My feet are stinging so much it's driving me nuts. I hope the bull doesn't come back until I get my socks dry. I'd like to take them off and stick them on the rad, but I don't want that big son of a bitch to catch me running around in my bare feet. I gotta get them dried out, though, before we head for a flop. I had enough grief getting here, and it's a hell of a lot worse outside now."

"Maybe it won't matter whether the bull comes back or not," I said. "That is, if you want to try it?"

"Try what?"

"See the bench parked in front of those two rads?"

"Yeah. What about it?"

"Plenty. See those radiators against the wall? They're about ten feet apart, and the bench sits against them 'cause it won't fit between them. It's about fifteen inches away from the wall—far enough for a man to stretch out on the floor out of sight. Climb behind the bench and put your shoes and socks against the rad to dry while you sleep."

"Yeah, but what the hell are you going to do while I'm in there?"

"Me? I'll borrow your racing form and put the figures on the ponies for you. I'll pick you a couple of long shots for tomorrow." I had to put the needle in.

"Racing form! Hell, man, you know the goddamn newsstand's closed. But I'm going to give your idea a shot. If I fall asleep, just leave me here and get yourself a bed. Even with dry feet I'm not going out in that storm again."

"Okay. I'll stay here until the bull puts the run on me. But I'll be easy to find tomorrow. After I get up and have a coffee I'll go to the library and find a book to read."

By then Boots was standing behind the wooden seat, holding his shoes and socks. "When I lay down," he said, "see if you can spot me."

He lay down. "Unless the bull gets nosy," I said, "there's no way he'll see you. You're good for the night if you don't snore. I'm going to stay a bit and warm up before I leave if the bull doesn't put the run on me."

I went to a corner and took a seat beside two adjoining telephone booths. When I was a kid I found sixty-five cents in the coin-return slot of the first pay phone I ever saw. Since then I've looked in hundreds of slots for hidden treasure but never found more than one coin in any of them. I tried these, too. No luck. But as I sat down I noticed that the space between the booths and the wall was at least sixteen inches—just enough room for a man to cram into.

I climbed in and went to sleep sitting up, resting against the back wall, with my feet against a rad. I don't know how long I slept, but I woke up with a scorching hot foot. I yanked my feet from the rad and jumped up—but that was worse. The soles of my heavy boots were hot as coals, and the added weight of my body drove the pain up to my asshole. Instantly, I dropped to my ass again, setting a world record for getting out of high-top laced logging boots.

"Enough of this bullshit," I thought. "I'm getting out of here as soon as my boots cool off." But just then people started coming into the station. I knew from the schedule board there was a train for Chicago due at 4:30 a.m., and I figured it must be that time. One thing I didn't want to do was climb out of my glory hole with a gang of people staring at me. So I crouched there, waiting for the train to come and the people to leave. But again I fell asleep. I was wakened by another louder hubbub. Doors were slamming, a train bell was gonging and people were shouting back and forth in the din. At first I thought I'd just taken a forty-winker and the ruckus was the train for Chicago. But two things disproved it. One, I saw daylight through the window. Two, every muscle in my body was cramped. I knew I'd been contorted for a long time. My body was screaming to get up and stretch, but the telephone booths were in use. To take my mind off my plight I tried to listen to the conversations, but the racket was so loud I couldn't. Finally, my body's pain prevailed. I just had to get up —so I did.

With my long, matted hair and clammy clothes, I must have looked like some sort of apparition, because all hell broke loose. A fat matron with her arms full of parcels was waiting to use the phone when I bobbed up six inches from her face. She let loose a scream that silenced the station and turned all eyes toward me. Her parcels flew as she shot up her arms and streaked through the waiting room. A young woman grabbed at her to calm her down but was knocked ass over applecart in the one-woman stampede.

The old broad was blasting through the door when she bounced off the railroad bull who was charging in.

Normally, if I stepped in a bear trap or fell down a well, my mind would shift into gear looking for some angle to make the fix, but this morning it stuck in neutral. I watched the antics of the frenzied woman until the cop got into the act. By then my only recourse was to bull it through. Scrambling out of the snake pit, I sat on the nearest seat to put my boots on. But my feet were puffed up like bloated toads from the initial roasting. It was agony squeezing my dogs into my high-tops. By the time I stood up the bull was heading for me with the woman in tow.

Realizing I'd blown my chance to escape, I sat back down to finish tying my laces. The big police boots stopped beside mine.

"Is this the man that scared you?" I heard the fuzz ask. I looked up.

"I think so. But his hair was bristling in all directions. This man has a cap on."

The cop yanked my cap off. "Well, how's he look now? If this bo was rolled up in a ball he'd be a porcupine."

The woman jabbed her finger so fast she almost poked my eye out. "That's him! You're right. It's him."

"Ain't you got nothing better to do than scaring women?"

"Maybe I am a little at fault, officer," I said quietly," but the lady's the one that caused the commotion, not me. Just now she nearly poked my eye out."

"I'll have none of that guff from you, boy. This woman has a right to be here. Not you. You're trespassing. This lady paid her fare, which gives her the protection of the railway while she's on their property. Now show me where you came from so sudden you scared the wits outta this woman."

I stood up and pointed to the space between the wall and the booths. The policeman took a couple of steps and looked into the hole. Then he checked my six-foot frame and shook his head. "You tramps could sleep on a clothesline as long as it was dry. I can't understand why you never work. What kind of a life is that? You're a young man, don't you ever want to amount to something?"

"Yes," I said, "I'd like to be president of the United States if I could, but I'd settle for any kind of work. I just came off a gandy job on the B. and O. three days ago. I worked there four months till the job ran out. I had my stake locked in my suitcase—over a hundred and forty dollars—'cause I was scared to carry that much money. The railroad gave us tickets to Chicago. And it must of happened when I went to the toilet on the train. Someone cut the bottom out of my cardboard suitcase, stole the money, stuffed the clothes back in and put the case back on the rack. I never noticed it until we got to Chicago and I took my suitcase down."

"You say you worked on an extra gang for four months? My guess is you were bull cooking?"

"You're right," I said innocently. "How did you know?"

"Hell, boy! Excuse the language, ma'am," he added hastily, remembering the woman. "I know because if I looked at your hands and found no calluses and asked how you could use a spike maul or shovel for four months and not get blistered hands, that's what you'd tell me. But your story's good enough. I'll not say you're lying. So finish lacing your boots and get out before I change my mind."

"Yes, sir," I said, bending to my boots. "I'll be out of here in nothing flat."

"Are you all right now, madam?" the policeman asked.

"Yes, thank you very much. I'm sorry you lost all that money, son," she said consolingly, and left.

I finished tying the lace, stood up and put on my benny. Heading to the door I was thinking about Boots missing all the excitement. What a yarn I'd tell him in the library. But Boots hadn't missed a thing. Awakened by the shouting, he'd stayed out of sight.

While waiting out the furor, he put on his shoes and socks, then peeked over the top of the wooden bench. The first thing he saw was the copper heading toward me on the bench.

Realizing I was one of the main characters in the play, he missed his chance to get out unnoticed. Instead, he just knelt there and stared. As the cop and I were walking toward the door we saw him gaping over the bench. He ducked down when he realized he'd been seen.

"Okay, you," yelled the cop. "Get outta there."

The whole crowd turned and stared as a new actor entered the drama.

"Yes, sir," said Boots, climbing over.

"Is he with you?" the angry lawman asked me.

"No, sir!" I said. "I never saw this guy before. Well, wait now, I did. Last night I was crawling over that bench to sleep there, but this guy was already there. That's why I went behind the booths."

"I think you're both lying," said the bull, "but what the hell difference does it make? Between you two and the storm, I've had a rough night. I'm too damn tired to take you to the lockup and spend an hour filling in forms. To lay charges against a tramp in this town you gotta go through more red tape than the governor does to pardon a killer. So I'm going home, climb into the tub and try to forget I ever saw you. Now get the hell out of here. Both of you. And a final warning. Don't even think of grabbing a train out of town. If I catch either of you bums within a mile of railroad property again I'll lay so many charges you'll be bald by the time you get out." He slammed the door behind us. We were free.

"He's not a bad guy, for a cop," Boots gasped, "but I wouldn't want to foul him up again."

"Then I guess you're not coming with me," I said.

"Whaddaya mean? Where the hell you going that I ain't?"

"I'm going to the roundhouse, to shower and shave in the change room," I said. "You coming?"

"Am I coming! Are you crazy? What gave you an insane idea like that?"

"The cop, that's who," I said. "When he said he was going home for a bath, I thought, You lucky bastard, it's me that needs a bath not you."

"Ain't you even going to give the big bugger time to get off duty? You want him to catch you bare-assed in the shower? Come on, let's go have a coffee first. That'll give him time to get off the property."

"Not me," I said. "I don't think we got a worry. The way I read it, if you were as tired as the cop says he is, would you plow through this snow checking on a pair of bos you'd just given a break to? Hell, no. You'd make out your report and head for home. You're a gambling man, Boots. You want to make a hunch bet?"

"No goddamn way! Who the hell's stupid enough to lay odds like that? Not me. That's at least thirty days for a bath if you crap out."

We'd been traveling single file on the snow-beaten path beside the yards. When the trail I'd taken forked to the roundhouse, I took it.

"You crazy son of a bitch, you really meant it. You are going to the roundhouse," Boots protested.

"You're right. But I'm going to do some checking on the way. I'll try to get a reading on the bull from the first rail we meet. If he tells us the cop makes an early-morning check of the yards, I'll turn around and go uptown. But I think he'll say he never does. If I'm right, there's not much risk and I'll go to the roundhouse. Are you coming or not?"

"Yeah," he said softly. "All my life I've done one stupid thing after another. One more won't matter."

When we cut through a string of boxcars we saw a checker working. We watched while he finished writing, tucked the clipboard under his arm, took off his gloves and blew on his fingers. When he walked another forty feet and stopped to write again we walked up to him. "That's a pretty cold job on a morning like this," I said as we approached.

"It's my hands that give me trouble. They get so goddamn cold I can't write. Thank Christ I'm through when I finish this train. What the hell are you guys doing roaming around the yard on a freezing day like this? There's nothing out of here until two this afternoon, and it's only a quarter past seven." He stuffed the board between his knees and banged his hands together.

"We had a little bull trouble," I said. "He kicked us out of the station, so that's why we're here. We were figuring on going to the roundhouse for a crap and wash, but we don't want to run into him again. Do you know if he works the yards in the morning?"

"Not him. The one we had before was a prick. He was never out of the yards. I think he got his nuts off using his sap on hobos. But this cop's a pretty good guy. He'll be making out his report now, ready to head home. There's a train for Chicago due in a few minutes. He'll wait around until it pulls out. You got nothing to worry about as far as he's concerned. But before you go can you do me a favor? I ain't got nothin' but makin's and I'm dying for a smoke, but my hands are too goddamn cold to roll one."

He took off a mitt and blew on his hand before shoving it in his mackinaw pocket and pulling out a bag of Bull Durham and papers. He handed them to me and asked if I'd make him a couple of fags. While I was rolling them, he said, "Make a couple for you guys, too. I'd give you the whole goddamn works, only I got to finish this train and write it up in the yard office. That'll take an hour and a half, and I'll need a couple of drags on the way home."

When I finished the cigarettes for him I filled a paper with tobacco before giving it to Boots to roll his own. Then we lighted up, three on a match, and left the checker to finish his work.

In the roundhouse we saw two rails on the move with lunch pails. Boots nudged me in the ribs and nodded in their direction. "Looks like they're going to the lunchroom. Let's follow and ask if we can use the shower."

By the time we got to the room they were sitting on a bench beside a long table opening their lunch boxes. When the door closed they looked up.

"Howdy," one said, and the other raised his hand. This put us at ease and we walked over to the table.

I opened with, "Good morning, men," and before I could ask if we could use the shower, the biggest one smiled and said, "Good morning? Where you been, boy? Didn't you and your mate just come from outside? What the hell's good about a morning like this? You and your pardner gotta be froze. Ya got humps in your backs like a cow getting the prod, and you're walking like a setter stalking quail. Sit down an have a cup of java. It'll make you feel like new men."

He took two mugs from a drawer and slid them to us before going to the possum-bellied stove in the middle of the room where a large pot on top was giving off a wisp of steam and a pungent smell of fresh-brewed coffee.

While he filled the mugs the other guy took the lid off a half-pound tobacco tin filled with sugar and gave it to Boots with a can of condensed milk. "Get that in ya, boy," he said. "There ain't nothin' better on a day like this 'cept a red hot mama and a shot of good corn likker. But this'll have to do, 'cause we ain't got nuthin' else."

We were sipping coffee, waiting for it to cool so we could drink it, when I noticed neither man was eating. Then it struck me: these guys were hungry but weren't eating because we were watching. So I said, "This coffee sure hits the spot. But do you mind if we wash up before we go uptown? We're hoping to make a couple of bucks shoveling snow off sidewalks for a store or two. We'll finish the coffee in the washroom and bring the cups back."

"Go ahead," said the big guy. "Make yourself at home."

We thanked them and went to the change room where we sat on a bench between the lockers and drank before we showered and shaved our kissers.

CHAPTER 15

ON THE WAY TO TOWN BOOTS ASKED, "ARE YOU SERIOUS? You really gonna try to get some sidewalks to clean? This ain't Chicago. There's no Carters in this town."

To needle him I said, "You're goddamn right. Never show your ass to an honest dollar."

"You really do mean it, you crazy bastard. You're gonna freeze your nuts off for a lousy handout from some tight-ass who'll hand you a half a buck and figure he's doing you a favor." Then he went into a funk and neither of us spoke until we reached the main gut where a couple of merchants were cleaning their sidewalks. Boots grinned sarcastically, "You're in luck, Legs. The guy we just passed looks like he's ready to throw down his shovel. Go back and ask if he wants somebody to finish the job. He'll be glad to give you half a clam to get inside and warm up. Stupid bastard don't know if he works harder he'll work up a sweat with that mountain of clothes he's wearing."

Still needling, I said, "We got lots of time for that. Let's scoff first. We can't work on an empty gut. After we put the nose bag on we'll come back and hit the stores."

"Whaddaya mean, we? I don't care what the hell you do, but I know what I'm gonna do! I'm gonna get a racing form, put the figures on a couple of horses, then find me a bookmaker. If we're gonna be here all day I might as well try and make an easier buck than freezing my ass off with a shovel in my dukes."

I figured it was time to pull the needle. "I'm not going to shovel snow," I grinned. "Never intended to. I wanted to get a rise out of you. And you swallowed the bait like a pike taking the hook."

"Screw you," Boots said, but he smiled.

We left the café in good spirits and were searching for a place to light when we passed a gray-haired old man cleaning the sidewalk in front of a second-hand-book store. I stopped. "Hold it," I said, grabbing Boots' arm. "This could be what we're looking for." He stopped while I returned to the old gaffer.

"Are you open for business?" I asked.

The old man looked up when he heard my voice, stood the shovel in the deep snow, took his mitts off, pulled a blue cotton handkerchief from the pocket of his overcoat and wiped his nose.

"It's a little early yet, but the door's open. My daughter's in there. She'll look after you."

I motioned Boots to follow. When we got inside, he said, "What the hell we doing in here?"

"Getting out of the cold. Do you want to walk around in snow up to your ass for an hour and a half? It's only eight-thirty. There won't be a pool room open till ten. You got any better ideas?"

"No, but how we gonna hold this joint down till then?"

"Nothing to it. People do it all the time. Grab a book and stick your nose in it like you're a bookworm. If you're not interested, make believe it's a dope sheet. It'll be ten before you know it."

The old man's daughter was coming toward us so we clammed up. She could have been a looker. Her creator had done a fine job of putting everything in the right place, but she masked her tall, slim figure with a shapeless high-necked dress that hung two inches from her flat-heeled shoes, and there was no sign of makeup on her fine-featured face. I tried to get a reading on her, but she got to us before I had her made.

"You gentlemen are early. The store doesn't usually open until nine o'clock, but my father came early to clean the walk, and I came with him. If I can help you let me know."

I was about to tell her we would browse around until we found something when Boots said, "Horses, ma'am. Have you got any books about horses? Not workhorses or ponies, but racehorses, something that follows their breeding and blood lines?"

I thought he'd blown it and felt like kicking his ass, but the woman put me at ease. She smiled politely before she said, "If you follow me, I'll show you where we keep the books about domestic animals, but I doubt if you'll find much about racehorses."

Boots saw the look in my eyes. He knew he was in for a blast, but he shrugged and tailed the girl. I followed along until I saw Gorky's *The Artamonovs* on the shelf. I took it down and opened it near the middle to scan a few pages. The words whetted my appetite, so I turned to the beginning. Boots could handle the horses himself; he didn't need my help.

After a few minutes I looked up to see how he was making out. He was sitting on a short stepladder with an open book on his knees. Watching him pore through it made me curious enough to see what he was reading.

"Looks like you found a book on the ponies, the way you're gobbling it up."

"Yeah! It's terrific. It tells all about how racing began and how they improved the horses over the last two or three hundred years. Do you know that all the good racehorses of today came from just three stallions in the Near East? It's all right here."

"That's good! But you can't very well sit here for an hour reading one book without buying it; this isn't a library. They welcome browsers because they're the people who buy books. When you want to read a book but not buy it, pretend you're browsing. Read it for fifteen minutes or so, then put it back and pick up a few others. Then go back and read for another twenty minutes before you go through the same routine."

Boots chuckled and said, "Don't worry, Legs. There's no need to play the con. The lady knows we ain't gonna buy no books."

"How the hell do you know that?"

"Because I told her. She's good people, Legs, and not hard to look at either, even if she don't know how to dress, comb her hair or do her face."

"What the hell'd you tell her that for? You're lucky we aren't out on our ass in the cold."

"Because I read people, that's why. You always say, when you meet somebody new, the first thing you do is put the make on them, and if the figures are okay, level with them. Well, that's what I did, and we can stay here all day if we like, but I'm not about to do that. I'm gonna try and place a bet or two when I find a book joint. Her and her dad make coffee at ten o'clock, and she said she'd make extra for us if we're still here."

"Blind luck," I said. "I suppose you thanked her and said we'll still be here at coffee time?"

"Sure. What else would I say? I remembered your crack about the snow up to my ass and said 'Yes, thanks.' "

I went back to Gorky and was well into him when the coffee came. The father brought it on a small tray with cream and sugar on the side. I creamed the coffee and thanked him. All he said was, "You're welcome," and left. I'm sure he meant it.

I read while I drank, and when I finished I took the cup and saucer to where Boots was sitting. "You're the man with the in, so I'll let you take the cups back and thank the woman. We better not leave right away. It wouldn't look good. I saw you talking to her while you were drinking your coffee. What were you gabbing about?"

"You know. The usual questions. Where ya from? How long ya been away from home? What kind of work do ya do? The same things ya always get asked, only she did it different. She didn't keep firing questions like she was nosy. She talked about things that led up to the questions and made me feel like answering instead of clamming up."

To get a rib in, I said, "It's a good thing we're blowing town tonight, because I think you've been stung by the love bug. Who's to say? She might even get you to the altar. When you think of the setup you'd have, that might be a hell of a good move. Just think, you could run two stores in one. The wife could sell books up front, and you could make book in the back room. Think what a hell of a good front you'd have."

"Don't be a wiseacre," Boots scowled. "You can't get a rise out of me. You know I don't give a damn about broads, except for a tumble in the sheets now and then. In about fifteen minutes I'm taking off. I'm gonna get a racing form and find a pool room till the books open. Then I'll find one and place a couple of bets."

"Pick me up when you leave," I said. "I'm going back and read the last chapter. I want to see how the story ends. Boots's timing was on the nose. I was starting the last page when he nudged me and said, "I'm going. Ya coming or not?" I closed the book, the last page unread, and followed him to the street.

We legged it to skid row, a small part of town with all the earmarks of a big-city slum: run-down storefronts, flophouses, bootleggers, pool rooms, beaneries, drunks and vags. Boots bought a form sheet at a corner newsstand. The newsy was a small, gabby guy with a clubfoot. He told Boots where he could place a bet.

"You can't miss it," he said. "Go down this street to the next corner and turn left. It's between a café and pool room. But you can't place a bet in the cigar store. It's a front. The action's in the basement: poker, stuss, blackjack, chuck, craps, and three guys writing sheet. It's the only book in town that lays track odds on parlays. When you get in the cigar store, go past the counter and you'll see a door on the right. Go through and you'll be in a narrow hall, then keep going until you come to another door. That's where you go downstairs. There'll be a big bruiser at the door, and he'll fan you for a rod before he lets you down. You got lots of time to spend on the scratch sheet. They don't spring the joint till one o'clock."

When we got out of earshot, Boots said, "What a character. I bet he knows every pimp and sharpy in town. Ya should feel sorry for a little crip like him, but he doesn't need anybody's tears. Ya see the way he gets around on that bum wheel hustling papers. He moves faster than most people with two good legs."

"Yeah," I said. "He doesn't let it throw him. He enjoys being useful. Look at him, and then look at us. Just a pair of fucked-up misfits that can't get our lives straightened out. We're too goddamned smug to take a job and move up the ladder the slow but sure way."

"Jesus Christ, Legs! I didn't think I'd start you on a goddamn lecture. You sound like my old scoutmaster—he was a preacher. But I'd sooner listen to a guy like our neighbor in St. Louis, a man named Paulson. He had a wife and two kids, a boy and a girl near my age. In the spring he'd take off with a carny and wouldn't come home until late fall. One time him and my old man were gabbing, and my old man asked him why he didn't take a job instead of lying around all winter, and you know what he told my old man? He said, 'Work is for horses and mules, and they turn their ass to it.'"

This philosophizing could have gone on all day if one of us didn't break it up. So I pointed to a candy-striped barber pole ahead, with a sign beneath that said: "Haircuts 25 cents." It had been weeks since my last haircut, and I decided to spring for a quarter and get one. It would give me somewhere to go while Boots was handicapping races. "I'm not going to the pool room yet," I said. "You go ahead. I wouldn't be any help picking a winner and I'd rather not be around if you blank out. I'm going to catch me one of those two-bit haircut jobs. I'll catch up to you later."

"What you gonna do after the barber's finished cutting your hair? Are ya coming to the pool room?" Boots asked.

"Not likely. You'll probably be in the bookie's by then if the big mug at the door don't put the run on you."

Boots' parting shot was, "Don't worry about me going to tap city. You got all the dough we picked up on the train last night. What I got don't amount to a pot full of cold piss if I blow it."

The barber shop had three chairs, but only one barber. There were no customers, and the barber, a man in his middle fifties, was sitting in the first chair, playing solitaire on a board across his lap. "Good morning," he said, "I'll be with you as soon as I set this board aside." He started to rise.

"There's no rush. You're almost finished. I'm not any busier than you are. I got lots of time."

"You're the customer, so if you say so I'll finish beating the devil." He picked up a curved stem pipe and put a match to it.

There was a Chicago paper on one of the chairs against the wall. I picked it up, sat down, turned to the sport section and was reading about a player deal between the Cubs and the Cards when the barber asked if I'd been in town long.

"Just passing through," I answered, and went back to reading. I wasn't about to get into a confab with him if I could avoid it.

"Going south or north?" he inquired.

"South. Seminole. Oklahoma. I hear she's booming."

"Yeah. I heard something about that. Oil ain't it? What kind of work do you do around oil wells? You look too young to be a driller."

"I'm a mule skinner. There's lots of work for skinners in an oil town if you can handle a jerk line." I went back to my reading.

But it wasn't long until I heard him snort in disgust, "How about that! Four cards to go and I can't get at the seven of clubs. Beats hell how close you can come to winning in this game before the devil strikes."

I looked up and watched him scoop up the cards, stand up and lean the board against the wall. "I'm ready any time you are young fellow," he said, motioning me to the chair. I went over and planked my ass in it.

"How do you want it? Long or short?" he asked, draping the blue-and-white-striped cloth over me.

"Not too much off the top and don't clip the sideburns. Just trim them with the scissors, and give me a clean line over the ears."

He was a good barber and, unlike most men of his trade, didn't keep flapping his lips. I kept reading the paper until a canned heater came in and put the beg on us for twenty cents, the price of a can of sterno. By his condition he'd already wrung out a can or two, and one more would knock him cold.

I dummied up and let the barber handle it, and he did a good job. "Sure would like to help if I could. But the truth is, I'd have to go hungry myself. Until I collect for this hair I don't have the price of a meal, and it's near time to eat now."

"Bullshit!" mumbled the heater and staggered out, slamming the door. When it slammed, the barber said in a sad voice, "You've got to feel sorry for the poor beggar, but giving him money won't help. He's finished, and there's more like him on this street. I'll bet he's not thirty yet, and he'll never see thirty-five. Between now and the time the city buries him in a pauper's grave the only times he'll be sober are when he's serving time in the county jail for vag or drunkenness."

The figures on the barber were toted up. He was high on the graph, right up there with the good people. First, he knew where his nose belonged and kept it there. Second, he didn't wag his tongue just to hear it clack. And third, he understood people's foibles without being a do-gooder.

I was tempted to drop it but had to say something to let him know

I knew how much it hurt to refuse the derelict the price of a can of heat.

"You're right," I said. "It doesn't seem there's anything can help them. It's not reasonable for a person to give up everything for a bottle of rubbing alcohol or a can of heat. But once in a while one of them gets things sorted out and makes a comeback, so there must be an answer some place, if people knew where to look."

The barber whipped off the cloth and I got up while he was shaking and folding it. As he draped it over the chair he said, "Better men than you and I have tried and failed, but some day someone's going to find a way to help. I think the repeal of the Eighteenth Amendment to start with."

"Yeah," I agreed, handing him a quarter. While he was ringing it up I asked how to get to the library.

It was just a short walk away. But during the fifteen-minute stroll my thoughts were scary. Were the past three years of my life a plus or a minus? Three years hopping from one boom job to another, with idle periods stretching into months, living in flophouses and hanging around pool halls. Was it three years wasted? It depended on whose figures you use, the tortoise's or the hare's. The tortoise would add it up minus and point out that to get through a forest you chart a straight course and keep plodding. The hare would say if you travel in a straight line you don't see much of the woods. But run fast on all the side roads and you'll still get there first and know what's going on.

When I struck out for myself three years before, I thought like a tortoise. I worked hard and was always willing to do more than my job called for, but it set me up. I was Mickey the bitch for everyone on the job. "Hey kid, you awake?" some asshole would call half an hour before the others stirred. "Will you feed and water my horses? I never got any sleep last night and I want to catch a little shut-eye before the whistle blows." The bastard had been up all night playing poker. And I'd do it for him, and harness his horses, too. But later, if I asked him to do something for me, he'd give me a bullshit excuse. Was it any wonder I started thinking like a hare? But today I was thinking like a dodo bird—one that didn't know whether it was a pigeon or a turkey.

CHAPTER 16

THE LIBRARIAN, A THIN LARGE-BONED WOMAN IN HER late forties, was sitting at a desk, bent over, making entries in a ledger. As I came near she plucked a pair of steel-rimmed glasses from her sharp-boned nose and put them on the ledger. Then she gave me a welcoming smile and beat me to the draw with, "Good morning." I thought of the rail's comment in the roundhouse this morning when I said the same thing, and had to hold back a chuckle.

"Yes," I said, "it has improved. The sun's out now, but it was pretty rough earlier."

I was heading toward the bookshelves when she said, "I haven't seen you here before. Are you new in town?"

"No, ma'am," I replied. "I'm just passing through and want to kill a few hours. And reading is as good a way as any."

I took another stride toward the shelves, but stopped when she asked, "Are you going far?" I wanted to answer yes and keep going but knew it would be rude.

"Far enough to get away from the snow."

"You mean you don't have a set place to go?"

"Yes and no. If I find a place I like I'll stay there for a while."

"You mean you don't know where you're going and have no purpose?"

How in hell, I thought, was I going to turn this woman off? All I came in for was to pass a few hours with a book. "I don't want to be rude, ma'am, but that depends on what your slant on life is. I'm not sure yet what purpose I want to aim at."

"I don't want you to think I'm reprimanding you, but you look very young to be out in the world alone. How old are you, if you don't mind my asking?"

"I'll be eighteen next June, but don't worry about me. I know how to take care of myself."

"But you must spend all your money just traveling around. Don't your folks worry about you, not knowing where you are and all? Do you ever write home?"

Jesus Christ! This old biddy was firing them now. Three questions without a breath. "I have no parents. They've been dead for some time and I don't spend money going from place to place. I beat my way. That is, I catch rides on freight trains, or on the engine of passengers if I'm in a hurry."

"It seems a shame to me, but I won't annoy you with more questions. If there's particular reading you're interested in, I'll try to help you find it if you wish."

"I've always wanted to go to sea," I said. "If you have a book of short stories about sailing I think I'd enjoy reading it."

She checked the file and said, "Go to the third aisle on your right. You should find one you'll like. What we have are on the second shelf from the top near the wall. There's quite a number to choose from."

I thanked her and went to the aisle. In a few minutes I found one I thought I'd like, took it to a nearby table and read for at least an hour before the librarian came and asked if I'd like a cup of coffee.

"Thank you. I was just thinking about going out to get a cup and have a smoke."

"Good. I put the pot on ten minutes ago. It should be ready."

She was back in no time, carrying a brown tray with two cups of coffee, cream and sugar and a salmon sandwich. "I took the liberty of making you a sandwich. You must be hungry. It's way past noon." She set the tray down.

Oh hell, I thought, here it comes again, but I thanked her as I put my book aside and picked up the sandwich and coffee.

"I'm not sure whether telling you my troubles will help," said the librarian. "You have your own reasons for living the kind of life you do, and I'm not about to censure you for them. But I believe, and I may be wrong, if your parents were alive you'd still be at home in school. I'm coming to my problem now, and it's the reason I asked you so many questions when you came in. I have a son one year older than you. He was always a good boy. He never gave me or his father any trouble, and he did well in school. Eighteen months ago, Gerald and his father had an argument, and I must say, I sided with

Steve, my husband."

I'd heard stories like hers before. The details might have been a little different, but the overall picture was the same. Gerald had a part-time job at a service station. He worked after school and all day Saturday for nine months and never missed a day—until he met a girl named Irene. It was love at first sight, as they say. They were never apart. In fact, Gerald quit his job so he could spend more time with her. His parents were unhappy when he gave up his job, but they didn't make a big to-do about it. A week later he told them he was going to quit school, get a job and marry Irene. Naturally, his parents were against the idea, with Gerald not even finished school yet, but there was no way they could reason with him. No matter what they said he'd fly off the handle and refuse to talk about it.

Irene's father was a prominent lawyer in town. Gerald's father, Steve, went to visit Mr. Gates, Irene's father, to see if he could put a stop to the engagement. Irene hadn't told her parents about her plans to get married, so, at first Mr. Gates thought Steve was jumping to conclusions. He laughed it off, but he promised to speak to Irene.

That same evening during supper the phone rang, and Gerald answered it. His parents knew from what they heard that Irene was not allowed to see Gerald any more. Gerald was furious. He called his father vile names and accused him of conspiring with Irene's father to stop the marriage. A hell of a row broke out, and Gerald stormed out of the house, saying he was never coming back. His parents waited up until daylight worrying about him but he never came home. He had gone to his friend Peter Morrow's, a boy he grew up with. Two nights later the boys left town on a freight train going west. His parents would never have known what happened if Peter hadn't left a note on his bed.

At first they thought Gerald and Peter would return after a few days. Time would heal the breach and all would be forgiven. But the days stretched to weeks, and nearly two months went by without a word from either. Then one morning Peter returned. He reported that he and Gerald had got as far as El Paso, where they were picked up by the police on a vagrancy charge and sentenced to serve thirty days in the county jail, which they did. Then they were told to get out of town.

Peter had had his fill of vagabond life and couldn't get home fast enough. But not Gerald. He was going to carry on to the west coast to find work and finish the job he set out to do.

He sent his parents a Christmas card, postmarked Corpus Christi. The note on it said he was trying to get a seaman's job on one of the ships, but he must not have got the job, because on his mother's birthday in May she got a card from Amarillo. He was still in Texas.

Sob stories are not my meat. Too many people dish them out with con jobs. But I kept my jaws locked and let Mrs. Cox unwind. I'd nod my head every now and then, the way I thought a good listener would, until her tale began to reach me. I knew she expected me to come up with something that would give her hope. But how was I tied in with her thoughts? What brought me into the picture?

My questions were answered when she finished by saying, "I know it seems foolish, but you'll grasp at anything and never give up hope if you want something bad enough. When you came in this morning and told me you were just passing through, I guessed you were hitching rides on freight trains and it made me think of Gerald. That's why I asked so many questions. Then when you were reading, a thought came to me. It seemed foolish, but I couldn't put it out of my mind. It was a notion that you might be able to help. God knows, I prayed enough for something to happen. There's a chance you might meet Gerald in your travels and give him a message from his father and me. His last name is Cox. Tell him we both love him, but not knowing where he is or what he's doing is breaking our hearts, and to please write if he won't come home."

I thought it pretty unlikely I'd ever get the chance to do what she asked, but it wouldn't have been kind to tell her that. Instead, I said, "I don't think the possibility of meeting Gerald is out of line." And, because I couldn't think of anything better, repeated the old saying: "The Lord works in mysterious ways." But even though I didn't believe it, I said, "I'll run into him, and I'll be sure to give him your message. All hobos hang out in the same places no matter what town or city they're in. Do you have a picture I could look at so I'll know him when I see him?"

"That's right," she said. "I never thought of that. I have a picture in my purse. I'll get it. It was taken two years ago and is a very good likeness of him."

I felt like a Samaritan as I watched her rushing off. The new hope had perked her up, which I liked, but it saddened me to know she had her money on a million-to-one shot.

"Do you think you should take the picture with you?" she asked.

"No, ma'am. I have a very good memory for faces. I'll know him when I see him, but it would help if you told me whether he's short, tall or medium."

"He's almost as tall as you, but he may have grown a little taller by now," she answered.

"I'll take that into account when I meet him," I said. "If he's grown I'll still know him."

I could sense Mrs. Cox getting ready to thank me. This I didn't want, but how to stop it? The answer came barging in the door. Four people entered, creating a disturbance. They were having an argument, and all four were trying to talk at the same time.

Mrs. Cox excused herself and hurried to see what the commotion was about. Here was my out, and I grabbed it like a hungover lush with a morning-after drink. I put the book back on the shelf, slipped into my coat, and took off. As I went by Mrs. Cox and the newcomers, I said, "Thanks for the coffee and sandwich, Mrs. Cox. I'll keep an eye out for Gerald, and with a little luck he'll be home before you know it." And I never stopped until I was on the sidewalk.

CHAPTER 17

THE POOL ROOM WAS LONG AND NARROW, WITH TWO tables abreast. They were strung out tandem, like a sixteen-mule team. Hanging over each one were lights with large green reflector shades. These lights were only turned on when the table was in use.

Six men were playing pea pool for fifty cents a pea on the first table, and two Boston players were banging on another—hoping that by shooting hard the ball would carom around the table and knock in another, because they couldn't play well enough to make a shot.

There were a few jokers sitting on high wrought-iron chairs that flanked the wall, watching the pea pool game. Boots wasn't among them. He'd be next door at the bookmaker's, and there was no way I was going to go looking for him. His absence was a good sign. If he'd tapped out he'd be in the pool room. I took a seat and studied the shooters. If the game looked like a pushover, I'd risk a buck or two trying my hand at increasing the bankroll.

They played two games. The same Joe that cashed the first game cashed the second. He was a stroke or two better than the others, but nothing I couldn't handle. I went to the rack and picked a cue, then walked to the table and said, "Deal me a pea. I might as well donate a few bucks to the cause."

The Joe doing the cashing spoiled that in a hurry. "Sorry, Mac," he said. "This is a closed game. We've never seen you shoot before. But if you hang around till this game breaks up, I'll play you straight pool for a few bucks a game. But you'll have to give me a spot until I find out how good you are."

"Spot, hell!" I said. "I saw you shoot a better stick than me." I knew I'd made him feel important in front of the others by the way he swaggered around the table before taking his next shot.

I returned to the chair and watched the big-time shooter and his pals. He was taking them to the cleaners. They broke the balls, and after three or four missed their chance to cash, I heard voices coming from the rear of the room. I looked around and saw two guys sitting in semi-darkness. One of them was Boots.

When I swung my ass off the chair and walked toward them they were so busy gabbing that neither of them heard me coming. The first words I heard were from the little character that Boots was chatting with. He was small enough to be a jockey.

"We should know in about twenty minutes. It's almost post time," he said. My "Hi!" surprised them. "You must have something good on the burner the way you're carrying on and grinning like a pair of striped-ass apes," I said.

"Could be," Boots piped up, all smiles. "Get a-hold of your left nut and hang on to it for the next twenty minutes. They tell me that brings luck. Me and—oh, by the way, Legs, meet the Swede. His handle's Eric Ericson, but his moniker's Swede. We split our case ace on a three-horse parlay, and the book paid track odds. The first two horses romped home in front, and paid big bucks. The first was better'n seven to one, and the second paid twenty-one forty for a deuce. So get a hold of your bag and hang on."

If I said the news didn't give me a charge, I'd be a liar. I rammed my left hand deep in my pocket and pulled it out. "No go," I said. "I gotta cut a hole in my pocket. Either you guys got a knife?" I was getting in the spirit of things. Swede shoved a wicked looking shiv in my puss. The shining six-inch blade was so close to my snoz it scared hell out of me and I ducked from instinct.

"At your service," said the Swede with a snicker.

Boots came on, his voice a little louder than usual. "For Christ's sake, Swede! Put that thing away. You goddamn near took Legs's head off. Ya got a draw quicker'n Jim Bowie."

Swede closed the knife and put it back in his pocket. "I practiced, that's how, but you don't have to open it. It's got a button, and zip, it opens when you press it."

"Practice? What the hell ya want ta practice a thing like that for? It could get you in a lotta trouble. Suppose you have to use it and kill somebody? What the hell ya gonna do then? You'll either swing or be gone for life."

"That's why I practiced so hard. I don't only know how to get it out fast, I know how to use it. I ain't gonna kill nobody, because I won't cut deep enough for that. I practiced that, too. I'm a few years older than you and I been working in camps since I was fourteen. I finally got fed up with taking a shit-kicking every time I spoke up for myself. Everybody picks on a small guy like me. So two years ago I got this knife and worked on it. Nobody's beat the shit out of me since, and I never had to cut nobody neither. Once I come up with the shiv and flash it around like an expert everybody backs off."

"You've made your point," said Boots. He looked at me. "There's a pretty good Kelly game up front, Legs. Funny you didn't spot it when you came in. You're a hell of a lot better shot than any shooter in it. Why don't ya go up and grab some easy bucks?"

"Yeah," I answered. "I tried to crash it, but there's a wise prick taking his buddies for a ride and he put a damper on it. He told me it was a closed game. But I'll play you a game of Boston and bank my game ball three cushions, or would you rather have a straight spot?"

"What the hell's the difference? You'll win anyway. All I got on my mind is Noble Dan. I'll play later when I can put my mind to it. I gotta find out if I'm in the chips before anything else. Come on, Swede, Let's go get the verdict. Ya coming with us, Legs?"

I walked with them as far as the pea pool game and said, "You two go. I'll wait here until you come back."

They were gone three quarters of an hour. When they came back, I knew by the look on Boots's kisser the news was bad, and Swede's hangdog look confirmed it. But I stayed mum, waiting for them to give me the word. "Come on," Boots said. "I'll shoot ya that game of pool now." He kept on walking to where we'd been sitting before, not telling me whether we were in the crapper or the clover. When he reached the spot where we'd been before he sat down.

He waited until Swede and I joined him before he said, "You'll never believe it, Legs. We had it won going away. We got there in time to hear them call the race on the radio. Noble Dan came to the eighth pole leading by two lengths and going away. The jock hasn't used the stick yet. He won by six and a half lengths with a hand ride. In my mind, I'm already in a notch joint banging a broad, when the guy on the radio comes out with, 'Uh-oh! They're posting an inquiry.' I lost my hard before the guy finished saying inquiry. For the next twenty minutes Swede and I sweated it out, hoping Noble Dan wouldn't be called, but he was, and they placed him last."

Swede showed the mark of a true gambler when he said, "I guess it wasn't in the cards the way my luck's been running this past ten days. It would be better, though, if Noble Dan had been an also-ran. That way you're dying with him instead of getting all charged up spending money you think you got and find out the check you're trying to cash is a stiff."

To shake the gloom I said, "Come on, get a stick and break the balls. Where do you turn on the lights? I'll play both of you."

Swede hit a switch on the wall and the lights flared on. "Count me out," he said. "I'm not much for pool, but you and Boots play. I'll watch."

We'd hardly started when four guys came in, peeled their coats off and hung them on the wall beside Swede. Then each took a cue from the rack, and one broke the balls. They'd had a few belts of lush and were arguing about money. Two of them, one in particular, the biggest of the four, was spoiling for a fight. And according to the way he was talking and acting, he didn't give a damn which one or how many he took on. He just wanted to do battle.

"What ya say we forget this game, Legs," murmured Boots. "The way that big bastard's pushing those guys around, something's gonna happen. He reminds me of Snake Wier in Chicago. When he got a few shots under his belt he was the snakiest son of a bitch you ever saw. He was the kind of guy would ask ya to have a drink and take you to the shithouse or alley or anywhere out of sight, pull a fifth from his pocket, down a big slug himself then hand you the bottle. And while you had your head back guzzling, he'd nail ya with a sneak punch in the chops."

"Yeah," I said, "but there's only five balls left. One of us'll probably run them on our next turn at bat. Go ahead, knock a couple in and I'll make the rest; then we'll move." That was a mistake.

Boots was so antsy he missed an easy setup and left the cue ball where I'd have to play my shot from between the tables. I studied it carefully. The balls were well spread out. If I took my time and bore down, I could clean the table. I bent over and was taking aim, stroking the cue smooth and steady, when the quarrelsome bastard bent over to take a shot. His ass hit mine and knocked me off balance, and I missed the shot. I was hot as a bitch in heat, but swallowed my curses and was walking away when the big ape grabbed me by the shoulder, spun me around, slammed his chest into mine, and growled, "You clumsy jerkoff, why don't you look what you're doing?"

I backed up a stride and retorted, "You're the clumsy asshole, not me! I was making a shot when you came charging around the table like a hound chasing a raccoon and barged into me." Then I picked up a ball with my right hand.

"You're pretty goddamned small to be calling me a clumsy asshole. Take a look at how wide these shoulders are," he said, throwing them back and sticking his chest out.

"Yeah," I said, squeezing the ball tighter. "You're wide between the shoulders, but you're goddamn narrow between the eyes." And I planted him there with the ball in my hand. It splattered blood all over his kisser when the skin on his forehead split, and he went down like a steer in a slaughterhouse when it gets the maul between its horns.

When I dropped him, his pals were on the far side of the table. Two of them, hell bent to avenge him, whipped around it to get at me. But Boots, clutching his cue in the middle with both hands, heavy end up, leaped between us and began taking wicked cuts at the air like a home-run slugger. "Hold it, you pricks with ears, or you're going to the emergency ward," he yelled. "I'll spill your goddamn brains all over this fucking pool room."

This put the shit up their necks and stalled them in their tracks until Swede got his knife in his hand.

"And your guts'll be on top of them," the Swede said, soft and cool, as he flicked the shiv back and forth with his arm fully extended, ready for a quick thrust.

Meanwhile, I wheeled to face the third guy, who'd dropped his cue and was charging at me with his head down like a hungry bull at a haystack. When he got to me he straightened up and threw a sucker punch that I stepped inside. Then, instead of jabbing, he brought his left all the way from his asshole. I stepped inside again, grabbed his shirt at the shoulders, yanked him forward, bashed my head into his kisser with a Scotch upper cut and followed with a right cross to the jaw. He put both hands to his face and took off around the table. I never pressed my edge. Instead, I turned to see how Boots and the Swede were making out with the other two guys. Nothing had changed, except Boots had stopped brandishing the cue and the Swede had dropped his knife arm to his side. The snake was back in the world and trying to get up. He was on his hands and knees, shaking his head from side to side.

I knew from the passive look of the other two that there was no danger from them. "Put down your club, Boots," I said. "These guys have seen enough to know they can't win. Let them get this snake on his feet. Maybe the next time he gets half cut he'll know he can't take on the world." I bent over to see how bad his forehead was gashed.

Meanwhile, the loafers watching the pool games had rushed to get ringside seats. The shooters, not wanting to miss the show, left their games and followed, with the owner legging it behind them. A loud, excited buzz came from the crowd, everyone talking at the same time. Finally the owner took over.

"Come on, you guys, the show's over. Everybody back to their tables. I'll handle this." As the men began drifting away, he turned to the snake who was now on his feet. "You guys came in here looking for trouble and got what you asked for. In fact, you got an overdose. Now get the hell out of here before I call the cops."

When the four jokers had staggered out and the pool room was back to normal, Boots and I put our coats on and the Swede went to the can. While we were waiting for him, I asked Boots how the two of them got tangled up. He told me he was studying the racing form when the Swede came in and sat beside him and asked if he could have a look at the Juarez entries. Then they got gabbing about horses. And after the Swede looked at the entries, he gave Boots a horse in the second. They were still gabbing when the bookie joint opened, so they went there together. The only winner, outside of the action they got on the parlay, was the Swede's horse at Juarez. "He's good people, Legs, and I know he's broke. Let's blow him to a feed."

We stopped to pay for the pool on the way out, but the owner wouldn't take the dough. "It's on the house," he said, with a grin on his kisser.

We'd finished our meal and were having a cup of coffee with our smokes when I said to Swede, "For a little guy you got a lot of moxie. You've been farther around the ham bone looking for meat than most people have been away from home. What the hell you doing in Joliet? You're too small to be a jailer at the pen, and that's about all the work there is here."

"I came here nearly two months ago to meet a cousin of mine. Him and I knock around together a lot. Rufe's a top mechanic, but like me he's a boomer. He's got tools in every hock shop between here and L.A. We keep in touch when we're not together. I been holding this town down waiting to hear from him, but something must have gone wrong. I think he must have got nabbed by a yard bull and got a stretch in some county jug for trespassing or vag. He knew I was coming to meet him, but he pulled the pin before I got here. He left a note with his landlady saying he was going to Kansas City and for me to hang tough here till I heard from him through General Delivery. But I've given up hope of hearing now."

"How much longer you gonna stay in this burg?" Boots asked. "Why don't you climb on the train and come to St. Louis with Legs and me? You can't get nothing to do here. At least in St. Louis you got a chance to ship out on a gandy job."

"I'd like to, but I'm going to hang in another week on the chance I'm right about Rufe. I'm doing all right. There's a fellow owes me a few dollars and he's paying off. The third day in town I got a job pearl diving from midnight to eight at an all-night café. The owner, a Greek guy, made book. He was a small operator that didn't know the score. Mostly he just took bets at noon hour from working stiffs that eat there. He had a big railroad watch he used to keep track of post times. About ten-thirty he'd take the watch from his vest pocket, unsnap it from the chain, put it on the shelf behind the cash register and leave it there until he closed the book. Then he'd put it back in his pocket.

"He had a sharp guy slinging hash on day shift, and him and I used to past-post the Greek once or twice a week. Next door there was a big book where you could listen to the race being run, The hash slinger would watch his chance and set the watch back seven or eight minutes. I'd hang around the book next door waiting for a horse to come in with long odds, then I'd rush to the café and put a fin on the nose. Then the waiter would watch for a chance to spike the watch ahead again, before the Greek picked it up and stowed it in his pocket. I was building up a small road stake when the Greek smartened up and fired us both. Larry, the waiter, went on a binge, got picked up and charged with being drunk and disorderly and the judge rapped him with a twenty-five-dollar fine or thirty days. He was a good Joe, so I paid his fine because he was broke flatter than piss on a plate. He's working and piecing me off with a buck or two when he has it, and if we're both broke I go to the beanery where he works, eat a good meal and he gives me a five-cent chit, like all I had was a cup of coffee."

We were on our third cigarette when Boots looked at the clock over the door. "It's nearly seven," he said. "Let's not head-end out tonight. We won't be lucky enough to ride the plush, and it's so goddamn cold we'll freeze our balls off before we get forty miles down the road. Let's go check the call board at the roundhouse and see if we can get a redball that'll put us in St. Louis tomorrow morning."

"Suits me," I said.

Outside we bade Swede goodbye and took off for the roundhouse. When we got to the yards a crew was making up a train. A snake standing by a switch was signaling with a lantern. We asked him if there was anything leaving for St. Louis tonight.

"We're making her up now. She'll be pulling out of here at twenty after ten. There's not many empties on her, but what there is will be in the middle of the drag, behind a string of tankers."

We thanked him for giving us the dope on the train and went back uptown to kill the next three hours in the pool room. The Kelly game was still in full swing, but with just four shooters. Only one of them had been playing in the afternoon. He gave me a nod of recognition and said, "Get a stick if you want to get in the game."

"What are you playing for?" I asked.

"Four bits on the cash and four bits on the kill," he answered.

"That's a little steep for my blood, but I'll play a few games," I said. I went to the rack and picked out a cue.

I was the last man to shoot and never got a shot. The third shooter cashed and moved me up a couple of notches for the next game. But when my shot came we were shooting the three ball, and I was hooked tighter than a bull's ass in fly time and never got another turn—another half a rock down the drain. After the next break I dropped back to fourth shot. In the third game we were up to the seven ball and everyone still alive when my turn came. My ball was fourteen. It was sitting dead in front of a corner pocket almost in the hole. A little nudge would drop it. I had an easy shot for the seven, and the balls were well spread out. It would be easy to run the table, win the game and pick up four kills on the way—a four-buck game. But I didn't want to open up. Neither did I want to keep dishing out four bits a clatter every time someone else cashed. That meant I had to knock the fourteen ball in by a combination or billiard shot and make it look like a fluke, so I potted the seven and played position. There was no way I could make the eight ball, but the cue ball was where I wanted it. I had an easy two-cushion billiard shot from the eight to my ball in the hole, and I made it. "That's it," I said, and tossed my pea on the table.

"You lucky bastard!" said the next shooter. "That's my eight ball, and you left it set up. Goddamn the flukes. They'll beat you every time."

Now I could relax. I was up a buck and playing with other people's money. I stayed in the game, playing it cosy until nine o'clock and time to leave. When I took a tally outside, I was eight-fifty in front.

Boots watched me count the money and stuff it in my pocket. "Not bad for two hours' work," he said. "You must have won a sawbuck or more. Why'd ya quit so soon? The train don't leave for another hour, and it only takes fifteen minutes to get to the yards."

"True," I said, "but don't you want a coffee before we leave?"

"Sounds good. There's two places on the way to the yards. You want to give one of them a try?"

"Yeah. Let's go."

CHAPTER 18

WE SPENT AN HOUR SHOOTING THE SHIT OVER TWO
mugs of coffee before we left for the yard. When we got there the
train was made up and waiting for the hostler to back the road hog
on it. But the crummy was on, and we figured the crew was aboard
because it was all lit up.

"It won't be long now," I said. "Let's find an empty and climb in
before she pulls out."

The snake was right. There were only three empties in the train,
behind the tankers where he said they'd be. We were opening the
door of an empty when we saw someone walking along the train.
Thinking it might be a yard bull we went to the end of the car and
hopped over the coupling to the other side of the drag. On a siding
three tracks away there was a string of empties. When we crossed
over to get to them, we saw that most of the empties had their doors
wide open. Inside one, sheets of heavy paper were spread on the
floor and up the sides, almost to the roof.

I pointed to the paper and asked, "Does that paper give you any
ideas?"

"You bet your John Jesus it does. When the bull goes by we can
roll it up and take it to an empty on the train."

It seemed like whoever we saw coming our way would never pass.
He finally got to where we could see his legs between the cars and the
tracks, but he paused for a few seconds every time he reached the
front of a tanker or boxcar.

"No wonder it took him so long to get here," said Boots. "He's no
bull! He's a train clerk writing up the train." Laughing, we climbed
into the boxcar and rolled up the six-foot-wide sheets that were
spread on the floor.

The door of the empty boxcar coupled to the tanker was partly
open. The doors of the other two cars were closed and sealed. They
had been unloaded from the other side. To avoid climbing between
the cars again, we tossed the rolls into the car with the open door
and I went to find a small stick. We spread the sheets on top of each

other at the front of the car to make a pad. The last one we tore in half and crumpled into pillows.

I left a three-inch gap in the door, then jammed the door with the stick so it couldn't be opened or closed from outside. I did this because I was once asleep in a boxcar and the shack, not knowing anyone was in the car, closed and locked the door. I damn near panicked when I woke up and found it locked.

It had happened in Saskatchewan. The car I was in was set out on a siding in front of four grain elevators in a small prairie town. I must have pounded and kicked the door for nearly five hours before the elevator man came to work and heard the banging. "Christ almighty, I thought there was a horse in there," he said when he opened the door.

We turned down half the paper sheets then took off our boots and coats before lying down on the pad and spreading the coats on top. Then we pulled the sheets up—and had a soft, warm flop for the night. It was going to be a good trip to St. Louis.

We were lying in comfort talking and smoking when the boxcar gave a lurch and we knew the hogger had backed the road hog onto the train.

"Won't be long now," Boots said. "We're coupled up. Soon's they get the air pressure pumped up we'll be long gone."

"It can't be too soon to suit me. I'm tired as hell, but there's no use sleeping before we start. We'll only be woke up when the hogger takes slack to get the train under way."

The air line began hammering, then stopped. And we knew the hogger was taking slack, because we heard the clashing couplings engaging. Then the car leaped forward. We were on our way. It was time for shut-eye, and we fell asleep to the clack of the wheels on the rail joints.

Two things woke us up: the train stopped, and the stillness was eerie. Outside it was still dark, but we had no way of knowing the time or how far we'd come. We thought of getting up and going out to check the score, but figured we were laying in the hole for a meet with another train. So there wasn't much to learn.

I put a match to my cigarette and said, "You know, Boots, I think you should get a job in St. Louis before you go home. You told me your folks always had a tough time putting bread on the table. If you did, you'd help them instead of making it harder for them and the younger kids."

"That's true," he said. "I been thinking that too, but you can't pick jobs off the sidewalk."

"You're right, but you could buy one at the slave market. I'm against it in principle, 'cause no man should have the right to peddle jobs. But sometimes you got to put your principles under the bed— out of sight, out of mind."

"Hell, man, you know how much I'm against buying a job," he said. "We've talked about it before in Chicago. And what am I gonna use for money? You're right, though. When we get there, I'm gonna get a job before going home, and I ain't gonna be choosy about the kind of job I get."

"I was going to keep the heat on while he was hot, but the long, piercing blast of the oncoming train's warning whistle distracted me, "Here comes the meet," I said. "It shouldn't be long now."

I fished in the pocket of the coat pulled over me, found the sack of Bull Durham and papers, and we both rolled another smoke. After we lit up, Boots took a drag and said, "Not bad, eh, Legs? Just like living at the Ritz. I wonder what the poor people are doing?"

"Yeah," I said, not wanting to get into a confab. I was thinking, and the thoughts were disturbing. What was even more unsettling was the fact that the same thoughts were plaguing me all too often of late. What were Boots and I doing with our lives? We were living one day to the next with no thought of tomorrow. If this was the way we were meant to live, why was man the only animal God gave the ability to create, and not just procreate? Men who lived the kind of lives we did were below the lesser animals. At least animals procreated. If everyone lived like us, the wonders created by man would never have come about, and the human race would soon be extinct because we didn't even procreate. In fact, we were a pair of nothings.

Boots was a healthy young guy. Like me, he should have been working instead of going home to eat his old man's spuds.

The whistle stopped and the echo came, followed by the hum of the rails and then the pounding of the wheels and the hiss of the steam escaping from the road hog's cylinders. The boxcar tipped in the slipstream of the onrushing train and shook from side to side like an old dog shedding water. Then it was gone and silence returned, but not for long.

The hogger grabbed the whistle cord, tugged it twice and the locomotive's two short blasts shattered the stillness. After the highball, the engine took slack, and the boxcar leaped forward. The slow drag out of the hole began. We were on our way again.

While we were crawling onto the main line we had another smoke, but by the time the shack closed the gate behind the crummy and climbed aboard, we'd butted out and settled back in the pad. We slept till the train stopped again. Light slashed through the slit of the door. It was daylight, and I was about to get up when I heard the highball.

Half asleep, Boots said, "We're taking off again. We must have stopped for water. I'm gonna catch me some more shut-eye."

I got up anyway and looked out. We were in a division yard and had stopped to change the locomotive and crew. This meant we were at least halfway to St. Louis. I took a piss out the door, rolled a smoke and went back to the pad.

While finishing the fag, I took another crack at Boots. I said, "The money to buy the job's no problem. We have enough. I've got over fifteen bucks in my kick, left over from the scratch we picked up on the train and the eight bucks I won last night. You can get a good job for a double sawbuck, so you should be able to get a helper or laboring job for the kind of hay we got."

"It wouldn't be right to spend that money to buy a job for me. You say 'We got.' But you're the guy's got the fifteen smackers. It's your dough, not mine. You promoted every goddamn nickel of it. I was just there when you hustled it. I even pissed away the fin I had betting on the nags at Joliet. If I was going to the coast with you I'd help you scoff up every fucking nickel of it, but that's different. A buddy doesn't see his pal go hungry if he's got a buck in his jeans, and the pal doesn't feel like he's sponging, because if it was him that was holding he'd dish out and think nothing of it."

Knowing how stubborn Boots was, I cooled it. St. Louis was six or seven hours away. There was plenty of time to put the hammer to the wedge. If I timed my blows right I'd have the log split before we got there. My final shot was, "I follow what you say: every man has pride. But kick what I said around. Don't close the book on it. Guys like you and I misdirect our pride." Then, to get off the subject, I said, "It must be between six and seven. When I was pissing out the door the sun was just over the horizon."

The train stopped again. We must have slept another three hours. We got up, looked out and saw we were in a small town. The main gut was only a block long, with vacant lots between its scattered stores and shops. The hogger, tallow pot and head-end shack were sitting on a low pile of ties eating lunch and sunning themselves near the engine. We were hungry and decided to go into town to grab a bite to eat. But the door on the other side of the car was locked from the outside. If we unloaded from the open door we would be in full view of the head-end crew. If they were hostile they'd tell us to stay off the train, and we'd have to skirt town and go up the track a quarter of a mile to catch it again on the fly.

"Let's gamble," I said. "The odds are in our favor. Not many train crews are hostile any more. If they're shitheels, we'll grab the train uptrack. The drag's long. The hogger's going to need more than half a mile to get her rolling fast." Boots answered by beating me to the ground and heading up the tracks. I followed.

We got to the crew and were about to ask if the train would be stopped long enough for us to grab a quick scoff, when the hogger asked, "How long you guys been riding?"

"Since Joliet," Boots answered.

"You must have froze your asses off last night. I hear it was two below, with a foot of snow on the ground up there," said the shack. "You heard right," I said. "There's lots of snow up there, but the ride wasn't bad. We kept on the move. Every time we started to get a little numb we got off our asses and ran around inside the car until we got the blood flowing again."

"You don't look the worse for it. Where you heading for?" the tallow pot asked.

"St. Louis. That's my home town. I'm going home. I've had enough of this tramp life," Boots told him.

"You'll be there about three o'clock, or a little before, if I get a good run at it and we don't have any meets," said the hogger. "There shouldn't be any, unless they run an extra north out of St. Louis."

"That's good news," I said. "We'll have time to go to the jungle and clean up before going uptown. We'll get to my buddy's place before dark. Do we have time to take on some chow?"

"Yeah, plenty," the Hogger said. "Our meet won't be for another fifteen minutes, then we'll be another twenty minutes because the siding's too short to hold the train. We got twenty cars and the crummy still on the main line. We're going to have to saw by."

It all went just as the hogger said it would, and about three o'clock we started seeing the outskirts of St. Louis. Coming into the east yards, Boots said, "This is as far as we go. We'll have to unload here and take a bus or walk. What say we have a coffee and figure what we're gonna do?"

"The coffee sounds good," I said, because I wanted to hit him again with my idea of buying a job. "We can ask someone in the café where to get a bus. But it's such a nice day I wouldn't mind walking part way if you know which way to head out."

We left the yards and walked a block and a half before I asked, "Have you given any more thought to what we were kicking around last night?"

"Kicking around? Oh yeah! You want to buy me a job."

"That's right. It's your money as much as mine."

"As a matter of fact I did think about it. If I had the money I'd buy a job because I'd like to give the other kind of life a try, and it would make my folks happy."

"Then it's settled. We'll head for the slave markets and see what they got to offer."

"Not so fast, old buddy. I haven't got around to taking your money. You're going to need every goddamn penny of it before you hit the coast. You're going through some hungry country. West

Texas is about as tough as they come. I know. I been there. The Mexicans are good people, but they're so poor they don't have enough to eat themselves. You're gonna need that dough."

"Listen," I said. "That's an insult to a bum like me. I been over that route twice, and I never had trouble keeping a full gut and getting a flop every night. In hungry country you don't beg the natives. You work the passenger trains over when they stop to unload and take on express. If you're not too timid to board the parlor car you're always good for a couple of bucks. Don't be a damn fool. Take the money and buy a job."

"You're breaking me down, ya son of a bitch. I'm about ready to take the dough."

"Good," I said. "Let's have a smoke." I pulled out the makings, handed them to him and clammed up. I'd pushed it enough for now.

We came to a café before we walked much farther. The waitress was a pretty girl about Boots's age. When she served our coffee Boots asked her where to catch a bus for downtown St. Louis. She was pleasant and smiled provocatively when she gave him the directions and told us we might as well wait a few minutes. "At this time of day it runs every twenty minutes, so one will have just passed."

Seeing the effect the filly had on Boots, I said, "Nice, eh boy? That, and more like her, goes with a steady job."

"Whattaya mean, 'goes with the job'? Who the hell says I'm interested?"

"I say you're interested. I saw the way your eyes followed every goddamned move she made. Why wouldn't you want a dish like that? But a tramp's got nothing going for him there. You got to be a solid working stiff to have dates with dolls like her. The way you and I are heading, we're going to wind up on the skid row with a thirty-five-cent bottle of derail for a girlfriend."

Boots grinned. "You never give up, you bastard. I'll take your goddamn money and buy a job. It's the only goddamned way I'm gonna get you off my back."

"Sold!" I said, and offered my hand to seal the deal.

He took it, and said, "You're still a bastard. But a good one."

It was too late to give the slave markets a play when we got off the bus, but we were up early and in the first employment office before ten the next morning. There was a long list of jobs on the board for skilled workmen: millwrights, machinists, polishers, buffers, barbers, waiters. Leading the list of unskilled labor was the old faithful, dishwashing. But who the hell wanted to spend eight hours a day with his hands in grimy dishwater, or peeling the jackets off spuds? There's no future in being a vegetable barber or polishing crockery smeared with catsup. Dishwashing was out.

There was only one job that looked to have good possibilities. It was a helper's job for an engineer. Boots asked about it and would have taken it but the going price was a double sawbuck. And all the money I had left, after paying for our flop and food the night before was fourteen dollars and change—six bucks short.

Boots tried to con the guy into taking a sawbuck on account and the balance when he got his first pay. The guy wouldn't buy it. He said he'd been clipped too often by taking promises, but it was a good job and would be snapped up this morning.

"For a young guy your age it's a hell of a deal," he said. "You get twenty dollars a week and everything found, even your laundry. It's in a mental institution. You fire the boiler and help with small repairs. In a year's time you can write for your third-class steam papers, and when you get them, come back here and I'll give you a job engineering. I'll tell you what I'll do, though. Give me two dollars' deposit and I'll keep the job for you until two o'clock. I can't be any fairer than that."

I whipped out two bills and offered them to Boots. He refused it, saying, "Where the hell we gonna get another six clams? You'll only blow the deuce. Let's try someplace else."

When we got outside I said, "You give up too easy, Boots. We can raise the money."

"Where?" He asked. "We don't even have anything to hock."

When he said hock a light flashed on in my noggin. Pawn shop! "To hell we don't. I'll have something to pawn in less than an hour. You want that job, take this deuce and give it to the man. But get a receipt in case he pockets it and doesn't keep his word."

"To hell with that, let's look around. But I don't think I could do as good anywhere else. It sure sounded like a good opportunity."

"Okay. We'll gamble the job's still there when we raise the money. Come on, we got work to do."

"Where ya going?"

"To find an undertaker. I saw a big funeral parlor when we got off the bus."

"What ya gonna do there to make a buck?"

"Maybe nothing, but I'm going to give it a shot. Come on, let's go to work."

The sign read Worral's Funeral Home. "You want to come in or wait out here?" I asked. "On second thought, I think you better wait. This won't take long. If I don't score here we'll try something else."

I went inside and was approached by a man in gray-and-black striped pants and a black jacket. "If you'll tell me the name of the deceased I'll direct you to where the body is resting," he offered.

"Thank you," I said. "I'd like to speak with Mr. Worral, please."

"I'm Harold Worral, Jr. Is it my father you wish to see?"

"It doesn't really matter. What I want is help in getting a job. I don't know whether you can help or not, but I hope you can. My uncle was a mortician. That's the reason I came to you. I been in town for two weeks looking for work but never found any. The day before yesterday my money ran out and I went without food until this morning. Finally I got so hungry I asked a man if he could help me out. He gave me a dollar, and he also said he had a job for me—as an office boy. I could start tomorrow, but I can't go to work in these clothes and big boots. I was wondering if you have any old clothes and shoes I might have?"

"I'm not sure what we've got," said the junior Worral. "But come along and we'll take a look."

He was good people, but he didn't fail to ask me the usual questions: how old was I, where was I from, how far did I go in school, why did I leave home? My stock answers must have satisfied him, because he didn't do any prying. He had only two suits, but lots of shoes. I was lucky. When I tried the coats on, the best one fit me best. Five minutes after thanking him, I was on the street packing a good pair of straight-last shoes and the best-fitting of the suits. He'd even given me a dress shirt and tie.

Boots took a gander and exclaimed, "Holy Christ! You really hit the jackpot."

"Let's get the hell out of here. Where's the nearest pawn shop? We ought to get at least a sawbuck for these. Look at the kicks. They're almost brand new, and so is the shirt."

The pawnbroker turned out the pockets of the pants to see how much they'd been worn, spread the pants and coat on the counter and checked for holes or flaws. "Six dollars," he said. "I'll give you six dollars for the suit, and a dollar for the shoes." And he started to tag them.

"No go! Ten dollars or nothing," I replied. I put the trousers over my arm and started to fold the coat. I figured I could get that much or more at one of the other hock shops.

"I'll give you eight dollars if you throw in the shirt. You won't get that anywhere; it's my final offer."

"Still no go, ten or nothing. There's two other pawn shops on this block. I'll go to one of them," I said, and picked up the bundle to leave.

"Wait, wait. You're in too big a hurry. Let me have another look. Remember, I have to sell them again."

I walked over to a rack of clothes, picked up the sleeve of a suit and read the price tag. "You're asking fifteen dollars for this rag and it's not near as good as mine, and I'm throwing in a good pair of shoes and shirt."

"So I'll be generous and give you ten dollars," he said as he opened the till and pulled out a sawbuck.

I grabbed the sawbuck, said "Thanks," and left.

"Here you are, Mr. Hawkins," the clerk said as he handed the envelope to Boots. "I don't think anything can go wrong. You should be able to start work right away. There's one thing I should tell you before you go. You will have to meet with their approval, but I don't anticipate any trouble on that score. Just give Mr. Partridge the envelope; he's in charge of personnel. I think the worst you can expect is he may ask you a few questions, which I'm sure you'll have the answers to. If anything does go wrong, bring this card back to me"—he gave Boots a green card—"and I'll either give you a refund or another position, whichever you prefer. Once again, good day, and don't let what I said upset you; we've never had any trouble with Mr. Partridge."

When we got outside Boots was like a bitch in heat. He really wanted the job. "I wish to Christ he'd never told me there could be a hitch. Now I'll be biting my nails till I know one way or the other."

"He was only giving you the low-down so you'd be prepared when you meet Mr. Partridge," I said. "Come on, let's get the bus."

"You mean you're going out with me? What about your train? You haven't checked it yet. You're liable to miss it and have to stay in town again tonight."

"I know when I'm leaving. I got nearly seven hours before the train pulls out. I'm taking the head end out. I checked the timetable we picked up in Chicago, and the passenger I'm taking doesn't leave until after seven. Of course, if you'd rather go out alone, we'll say our goodbyes now."

"Ya know goddamn well I want you to come, so why ya acting like that?"

"Good. I wouldn't want to sweat it out all the way to the coast not knowing whether you made it or not."

Boots was gone for an hour and a half. I read it as a good sign. He came out like an over-inflated balloon, ready to burst. It's a good thing I was there, for he needed an outlet or he'd explode.

"Jesus Christ, Legs, have I got it made! What a setup. I'm on the payroll now. They gave me a tour. You should see the big room I got. I even have a telephone. It's for emergencies, but I can make outside calls. Terrific scoffing. I already scoffed, and I ate like a horse. I'll be three hundred pounds in six months if I don't watch it. The guy I gotta help is about forty. I didn't have much time to read him but he seems like good people. He's got an emergency on the third floor. They had to shut the water off. He needs me now, but I told him I had to say goodbye to my buddy who was waiting outside."

I couldn't believe how steamed up he was about the job. I felt good because I'd helped him get it. "Great, that's terrific," I said. "Another tramp's finally got work ways. When I come back through, I'll look you up for a handout. You'll probably have your engineer's papers by then. You'd best get on the job. You can't have those people on the third floor using toilets with no way to flush them." I stuck out my hand. "I hate goodbyes, so let's just say 'So long.'"

Boots grabbed my hand in his and held on while he said, "Not so fast, you unsentimental son of a bitch. The last thing in the world I want to do is say goodbye. You're the best thing ever happened to me, and my parting shot to you, you preaching bastard, is listen to your own preaching. Go into St. Louis and get yourself a job."

CHAPTER 19

THE PARTING HAD BEEN HARDER THAN I THOUGHT. I'd split from plenty of road buddies before, and many of them I was glad to shake. Our relationship since that snowy day in Chi had been a good one, but the short jaunt to St. Louis had cemented our friendship. With the parting I was alone in the world again. It's hard for me to explain the feeling to anyone who has never experienced it. You're empty. There's nothing inside you. It's not the empty feeling your belly gets when you're hungry. It's a gut feeling that starts at your toes and flushes everything out the top of your head. The world is full of strangers, all of them making it because they fit in the jigsaw puzzle. The pieces are all in place and the picture's complete, but there's a piece left over. It's you—and there's no place for it.

I waited at the bus stop, but walked away when it came. It would get me back to skid row too quick, and that was the last place I wanted to be right then. I wanted to deal with my feelings on my feet, not on my ass, so I walked. Loneliness can break a man's spirit more severely than cruelty; in fact, it is a form of torture. The loneliest place on earth to be in and feel unwanted is a city of a million strangers. I thought of the trappers in my home town in northern Alberta, where I lived before my mother died and I went to my relatives in Saskatchewan. I used to feel sorry for the trappers when they came to town in the spring to sell their winter's catch. They'd stay sober until they sold their furs and bought their next winter's rations. Then they'd go on a bender until their stake was gone.

The town was too small to boast a red-light district, but every year—and they timed it on the nose—two or three whores would come from Edmonton and take rooms above the Chinese café. The trappers would give them a big play. The town's busybodies always got up in arms and talked of running the whores out of town, but nothing ever happened. In fact, some of them were even seen sneaking up the back stairs of the café.

I used to watch the trappers leave and feel sorry for them, thinking how lonely their lives in the bush must be. When I grew old enough to talk to them I found out I was wrong. It was when they were in town that loneliness booted them hard. The only friendship they got was bought and paid for with hard cash. In the bush they weren't lonely because they had an affinity with nature stronger than a man's love for a woman. They had to remain alone with nature or suffocate, and they spent a contented life in the wild.

The trappers had their way of life and lived it to the full. Maybe, I thought, I should take the four bucks in my kick and find a whorehouse. And I would have, only I knew I would get better value for my money if I used it for a road stake. Thinking about the road stake and how small it was, and noticing I was meeting people at the rate of two a block, I thought I'd try and pick up a little more change for the road by doing a little stemming. To be occupied might ease the empty feeling.

The first guy I dinged gave me a tin ear. All I got when I spoke to him was the freeze—he never broke stride. The next was also a tin-eared bastard. I was about to make a sarcastic crack when I thought about Phoenix.

I was there waiting for a highway job to break and holding the town down with another Canuck called Blackie. The town was overrun by working stiffs who were there for the same reason. This made stemming tough, because the natives couldn't venture out on the stem without getting the rigging put on them three or four times in a block.

Blackie was a sailor. He'd been in every major port in the world but couldn't bum salt, and I was doing the hustling for both of us. You could get a bed in a flophouse for two bits. Or if you didn't have the price, you could flop in one of the town's cotton gins. Most boomers spent their nights there, because a quarter was hard to come by and the nights were cold.

The cotton gins were a good flop. You could burrow yourself in the soft cotton and have a warm and comfortable sleep. The trouble was that when you woke up you were smothered in cotton. It stuck to your clothes, hair, eyebrows, and the hair in your ears and nostrils, and it took half a day to get rid of the lint.

Things were going tough this night. I had my flop dough and must have dinged fifteen guys, but all I got was turndowns and tin ears. "I've had it, Blackie," I said. "It's the cotton gin for you tonight unless you get out and kick your feet to get the price of a flop for yourself."

"Jesus, Legs! I can't bum. Come with me and we'll double up, and I'll do the asking," he coaxed.

Things were going as bad for Blackie as they had for me. He dinged four tin ears in a row. "Fuck this," he snarled. "I've had enough! If I keep on, I'll knock one of these tin ears on his ass and we'll both wind up in the can."

"Come on," I said. "You got to expect that. You can't win 'em all. Those guys you're putting the ding on don't know you from a windrow of assholes. They resent you putting the bum on them. They figure they work, and so should you. Keep your cool and try a couple more, and if you don't score I'll take another crack at it."

He drew a turndown and another tin ear. The guy stopped, gave Blackie a contemptuous look and started to walk away without speaking. Blackie grabbed him by the shoulder with his big left paw, spun him around and shouted, "You tin-eared son of a bitch, I'm talking to you."

The tin ear sputtered and came out with, "What do you want? I don't know you. Why are you bothering me?"

"You know goddamn well what I want. You heard me before. I want two bits, that's what I want, and I don't want any fucking no, I've had enough of them already," said Blackie with fire in his eyes.

The poor little bastard almost tore his pocket getting a quarter out and meekly handing it to Blackie. He took off fast, and we high-tailed it too, in case he hollered copper.

Thinking of Blackie's caper put me in a better frame of mind. I would have kicked my own ass if I could have for becoming such a sentimental slob over the loss of a buddy. Now my head was back on the main line and I was able to open the thinking throttle. I became aware that I was hungry. The business district had petered out and I was in a middle-class residential area. I walked for two

blocks before deciding to bum the lady of one of the houses for a
handout, or a sit-down if I was lucky.

The house I chose was a two-story frame house with a big fenced
yard. The gate was open, so I went to the back door and knocked.
After two minutes I was about to leave when I heard a slight stir
inside. I knew from experience that many women won't open the
door to a stranger and thought that was why I got no answer, when
suddenly it opened. She was a blonde woman in her late twenties.
She wore a long velour wraparound, with no sash. She opened the
door with her right hand while she held the dressing gown with her
left. Her swept-back hair was neatly combed, pony-tailed in a silver
clasp. Her beauty stunned me, and my mind took a tack off course.
Hunger was forgotten, replaced by a different appetite.

"I'm sorry I was so long," she said. "I was in the tub."

Like a stable boy before a queen I was speechless a few seconds
before I muttered, "Pardon me, ma'am; could you help a hungry
man with a bite to eat?"

She noticed my embarrassment and smiled. "I'm sorry," she
said. "I'm afraid I don't have much to give you."

"Just a slice of bread, anything at all."

"Very well. Come inside. I'll see what I can find."

"Thank you, ma'am," I said, stepping through the door.

When she closed it she pointed to a chair. "I'll be right back. I
have to find a sash. Make yourself comfortable."

I sat down without replying. I wanted this woman and was afraid
I'd do or say something dumb. The front of my strides was sticking
up like the center pole of a circus tent. I knew she'd notice it when
she came back, so I put my cap over it, but it was still obvious
something was holding my cap up.

My hands were clammy with sweat and my breathing was giving
me trouble. Christ, I thought, if I could be arrested for what I'm
thinking, they'd hang me for rape! I remembered big Jim Morrison,
a farmer I worked for in Texas. He was framed on a rape charge
and served eighteen months before the guilty man confessed to the
rape he was serving time for.

Jim Morrison was fifty. He was also a good husband and father.

He and Sarah, his wife, raised two sons and a daughter. All were married and doing well. There was only one thing Jim could be faulted for. He liked his drink and couldn't hold hard liquor. He never drank socially because one drink led to a prolonged drunk. But once or twice a year Jim went on a two- or three-day bender and he always wound up drinking at Carol's place.

Carol was the town whore. She had a bad start in life and never married. Her Uncle Ted got her maidenhead when she was thirteen. She was lucky for two years, but then she got pregnant. She had spread her legs for so many men and high school seniors in the interim there was no way she could finger any one guy, so she had to take care of her daughter herself. The upshot was that, after the baby was born, Carol found out she could get paid for what she was giving away, and there was a demand for it.

Eva Ann, Carol's daughter, was sixteen and retarded, with a woman's body and the mind of an eight-year-old. This forced Carol to keep a constant eye on all Eva Ann's associates and movements. She forbade Eva Ann to come into the business area of the house when there were patrons present, because the few times the girl wandered into the parlor Carol saw the lascivious stares of the men in the room, and it reminded her of the look on her Uncle Ted's face when he raped her.

There was no need for Carol to keep other girls, except during spring planting and fall harvesting seasons. The rest of the year, because the town was not large, Carol was able to take care of the half-dozen daily tricks herself. But to provide for herself and Eva Ann, plus the maintenance of George Blake—her free-spending pimp—Carol was forced to sell booze on the side.

She had no trouble with the law because she ran a well-disciplined house. But there was a slight payoff. Twice a week she had to rendezvous with the sheriff at a place of his choosing. On these occasions her cleaning lady, an ex-prostitute with a weakness for gin, would look after Eva Ann and tend bar until Carol returned from meeting the sheriff—which usually took three or four hours because the sheriff was a virile widower.

One evening Jim Morrison showed up drunk just before Carol

left for one her biweekly trysts. Edith, the cleaning woman, had already arrived and was downing her second shot. Dubious about trusting Eva Ann and the place in Edith's care after she'd had a drink, Carol said, "Edith, I don't like to leave. But I'll trust you if you give me your promise not to take another drink until I get back."

"Don't worry, Carol. I swear I'll not touch another drop until you get back," Edith promised.

Meanwhile the pimp, George Blake, went to tap city in a poker game before nine o'clock. Unable to get another stake from the house, because he owed a previous one, he went to Alf's, a blind pig where his credit was good. He knocked back four neat shots before Alf said, "Sorry, George, you're cut off until I see the color of your money. Your tab's getting pretty big."

"What the hell's the matter with you? You know I'm good for it," Blake snarled.

"Maybe so, but until I see proof, your credit's off," Alf replied. Pissed off with Alf and life in general, Blake went home. He used the back door because he made a point of never associating with Carol's clientele. He opened the door to uncommon quietness and soon found out why. Edith had fallen off the kitchen chair and was passed out on the floor. The only other person there except Eva Ann, who was asleep in her room, was Jim Morrison, flaked out in the front room. He put the frisk on Morrison and rolled him for forty bucks.

There was no need to stay home now. He'd have a drink then go back uptown and show those tight-assed bastards he wasn't chopped liver. He downed three fingers of moonshine and was at the front door when Eva Ann came to mind. He'd had a hard-on for her for more than a year, hoping for a chance to score. But Carol was always too vigilant. Now he had a clear field. Carol would be gone for another hour, and the drunk wouldn't bother him.

When he closed the bedroom door, Blake undressed slowly, then groped his way to the bed, and eased himself into it without waking the girl. But when he lifted her nightgown and started to fondle her she sat up and screamed. Blake silenced her with a right to her jaw that knocked her out and broke it.

He knew the penalty for rape in Texas was the noose, so when he'd had her he dragged Morrison into the bedroom and stripped his clothes off before putting him in bed with the unconscious Eva Ann. Then he returned to town.

When Carol came back, she was trying to rouse Edith when she heard Eva Ann whimpering and rushed to the bedroom. Eva Ann was sitting up, holding her face and weaving from side to side in pain. Her shredded nightgown was on the floor, and big Jim was lying naked beside her.

When she failed to comfort her incoherent daughter, Carol left her long enough to call the doctor and sheriff. She left everything the way she found it because she wanted the sheriff to see everything exactly the way she had.

Jim Morrison was given a speedy trial and got life. But after eighteen months in the pen, he got a break. Blake and two of his buddies heisted a bank in Waco without casing it and were caught by the law. One cop and Blake's pals were shot in the shoot-out. Blake was sentenced to death. On death row a preacher visited him daily and finally got him to accept the Lord. On the eve of his execution he confessed to the rape of Eva Ann.

These memories were rushing through my mind when the blonde looked at my lap and asked, with a faint smile, "Do you find it warm in here?"

I stammered, "No, I'm fine."

"Then, let me take your cap," she said as she whipped it off me. I tried to grab it, but she was faster.

"Well, what have we got here?" she asked, patting my tent pole. "It looks like there's another hungry man here needs looking after. Who do you think I should look after first? You or this fellow?"

I sputtered, "Do you mean? . . ."

And she said, "Yes, I mean! Do you want me now or after you eat?"

"But what if? . . ."

"Oh, stop it," she said, putting a finger on my lips. "There's nothing to be afraid of. My husband's out of town, and I don't have children or nosy neighbors. Come and get in the tub. I'll run the water for you." Silently I followed her to the bathroom.

"Do you like it hot, or should I run it cold to cool that fellow down that's giving you so much worry?" she laughed.

"Not too hot," I snickered while I fumbled with my shirt.

"Here, let me do that. The way your hands are shaking you'll be all day."

I undid my belt and was starting on my fly when she slapped my hands away. "Hey, let me do that. I want to be the one to free your friend and let him see what I got for him." She untied the sash of her kimono and let it swing open.

I got in the tub as she sat on the toilet seat and watched me. "Seriously, have you ever had a woman before?"

"Yes, ma'am," I said. "But they were all whores. It's not the same."

"What's the difference between fucking a whore and a woman that does it for pleasure?"

"I don't know," I said. "I guess it's all in the mind. I never got worked up over any woman like this before."

"Doesn't my boldness make you think of me as a whore?"

"No, because you want it as much as I do. A whore only does it for money."

"Let me wash your back. I'll bet the last woman that washed your back was your mother."

When she finished scrubbing me I got out of the tub, dried off and started to put my clothes on.

"Don't do that," she said. "There's no one here to see you except me. I've seen all you got and I want it. Let's go to the bedroom."

I came so quick I was embarrassed. I said, "I'm sorry, but it's been a long time since I've been with a woman."

"Don't feel bad about it," she murmured. "I'll get it hard again, and you'll have more staying power next time. I'm looking forward to that. By the time we get cleaned up you'll be ready again, and this time it'll be better. You'll see."

She douched and I washed, and she was right. As soon as the warm water came in contact with my prick it boomed up like a guy derrick. I stayed in the saddle far longer the second time and figured I'd done a good job. But the third time I found out what fucking was all about.

I'd been banging away about five minutes when the woman began moaning and writhing like a snake swimming upstream. I thought I was hurting her until she grabbed the cheeks of my ass and tried to thrust me deeper inside her. Then she began nibbling my nipples and beating me on the shoulders with her fists. I was going out of my mind with lust when we both came, and it felt like the soles of my feet were coming out my cock. I started to get up but she held me. "Just lie where you are for a while," she said, and I stayed until I grew limp.

We were still in bed when she said, "I can tell by the way you talk you're not from St. Louis. You sound a little like a northerner. Is that where you're from?"

"I'm Canadian," I said. "I come from a small town in northern Alberta, but I lived for a while in Saskatchewan."

"You're a long way from home. How did you get way down here? Are you going to stay in St. Louis long?"

To make it short I said, "I'm pulling out tonight. I'm going to California to get away from the snowballs."

"Do you have to leave tonight? You know what? We've been making love for two hours, and we don't even know each other's names. Mine's Nancy Evans. It was Carlton before I married Carl. I wish you weren't leaving town."

"Nancy. I like that name. And I like the person who's got it for a handle," I said. "Everyone calls me Legs, and I might be persuaded to stay in town if the right party asked me to."

She threw her arms around me and gave me a hug and a long open kiss. Then she drew back and said, "Now you've been asked the best way I know how. Will you stay?"

I couldn't say no. Nothing like this ever happened to me before, and I had to draw another card. It was like making an inside straight with two aces staring at me across the table—knowing she was married and there was nothing to look forward to but trouble.

"I'll stay," I said. "But I don't know how long. I have no job and no money. Tomorrow I'll try and find work." I said I'd hang around as long as I could, but I warned her she was asking for trouble. "Don't forget you have a husband. You're the one that stands to lose the most. You could lose your home, while all I got to do is catch a freight."

She dismissed my warning with a shrug. "If you knew how sex-starved I am you wouldn't think I was losing very much. Carl is a salesman. He leaves here Monday morning and I don't see him again until Friday. I'm lucky if we have sex more than twice a weekend, and then it's just on and off. It doesn't last more than five minutes, with no loving before or after."

It was dark when I kissed Nancy goodnight, with a promise of more of the same. I had a steak beneath my belt and her phone number in my kick.

CHAPTER 20

I SPENT THE NIGHT IN THE FLOPHOUSE WHERE BOOTS and I had bedded down the night before. The day's events kept running through my mind, and I had a problem sleeping. Life has a way of keeping the tally even. It knocks you down and kicks you in the ass, then picks you up like a mother and caresses the hurts away. At midday my spirits were lower than whale shit. Now they were soaring in the stratosphere. I was having trouble with the governor, the voice from inside that opens the switches to the track you take. Common sense told me not to become involved with Nancy Evans. But the memory of the afternoon, and the possibility of more like it, opened the throttle and sent me hurtling down the main line—and there was no way I could close it. Finally, I fell asleep balling the jack with the throttle still wide open.

I was up early, had a good breakfast and walked the six blocks to the government employment office, arriving twenty minutes before it opened. There were already forty or fifty guys there, queued up half a block from the door. They stood close to the walls of the buildings, while a big burly cop kept them from blocking the sidewalk.

I nodded to the last man in line and stood behind him. He returned my nod and said, "With all these guys in front of us we're going have to move fast to get close to the rail."

"I've never been here before," I said. "What's the rail got to do with it?"

"That's where they hand out the jobs. If you're too far back they can't reach your card when you hold it out. There's three clerks inside the rail with telephones, and when a call comes in it comes to them. They write down the information and come to the rail where everyone is holding out his card. They choose one or two, maybe more, depending how many working stiffs are needed. Then they go back to their desk, take your name and address off the cards and write it on a filing card. When they finish they bring your card back with a paper telling you where to go and who to ask for. But if you don't have a card there's no rush. You have to go to another place to fill out a form to get one."

"Thanks for smartening me up. What's a man's chance of getting work?"

"Not good," he said, shrugging. There were twenty or thirty men for every job that came in, he explained. Most jobs were part time and only lasted one or two days—maybe a week if you were lucky. He admitted that he was pretty lucky. "When I get a job, even if it's only for a day, I work like hell, and before I leave I always ask the foreman if he'll ask the employment office for me next time he needs a man. So I get my name called often. That way I make enough to get by on."

There would be a mad rush inside, he warned—with everybody trying to get to the rail first and no cop in there to keep order. Then he filled me in on the procedure for getting a card. "If you go to the right, there's no rush on that side. You'll come to two men sitting at desks inside a railing. One of them will give you a form and show you how to fill it out."

I was going to thank him again, but the line started moving and we moved with it. Everyone going left was in high gear, high-tailing it for the railing like hogs to the trough when they hear "Soowee! Soowee!"

There was only me and another guy going right. I went to one of the two men behind the desks. He looked skeptical when he gave me the form. "Take this over to that table, fill it out and bring it back," he said. "If you need any help come back and see me."

I had no trouble with the form. After five minutes I took it back and gave it to him. He looked it over and set it down. "I see by this you're only seventeen. This isn't the youth department; that's upstairs. Go outside, there's a door going up. Ask for Miss Cooney. She'll look after you."

That pissed me off. "Don't give me any of that kid stuff, mister. I been doing a man's work for three years. If you worked alongside me for eight hours, your asshole would be hanging so low you could cut washers off it."

I thought my hothead remark had blown it, but he merely

chuckled. "No need to get angry, son. I was only thinking of you. I've sent lads on jobs too tough for them, and they got fired in less than two hours. And when the company called for a replacement they told us to send a man not a boy."

"You don't have to worry about that happening to me. I've worked at everything from mule skinning to harvesting. The last two years I harvested, and when it came threshing time I spike-pitched, because it's the toughest threshing job there is and pays a dollar a day more."

He nodded. "I have to admit you're big enough, but size don't mean everything. Some big men ain't suited for hard work with their hands.

"That's true," I said. "I found that out when I worked in gangs. There's always one or two guys that don't keep their end up. And it's not the little guys, because the foreman always has his eye on them."

"You're not from these parts are you?" he said as he fished a pocket-sized card from a drawer and put it in the typewriter.

"I shipped out of Chicago to a gandy job at St. Charles. It wound up three weeks ago. I was swinging a twelve pound-spike maul for ten hours a day, six days a week. I like spiking, because when you get the knack of it you only have to pick the hammer up, let it fall, and snap your wrists. The maul does all the work."

"You've sold me," he said, whipping the card from the typewriter and handing it to me. "Take this to the other side and join the mob. If you don't get a job today don't get discouraged. Come back tomorrow, but come early and get close to the railing."

After thanking him I joined the crowd on the other side of the room. Two calls came in for men, but I was so far from the railing I didn't hold out my card. I would have left, but I had no place else to go. Then I noticed that neither clerk took cards from men against the railing. They always chose cards from the outstretched hands of men two or three rows back. So I edged my way a little deeper into the crowd when the guys that got jobs pushed their way out. While I was doing this, the guy that gave me the card came over, gave one of the clerks a slip of paper, then went back to his desk. A minute later, the phone rang. The same clerk picked it up and began writing. When he finished he came to the rail holding the slip of paper the clerk I'd talked to gave him. And to my surprise he called out my name.

The clerk I'd been a smart-ass with had come through for me.

"Right here!" I shouted, holding my card in the air.

I waited for him to process it, anxious to find out what kind of job I was getting, hoping I'd hit the jackpot and get more than a day or two's work. It was only minutes before he came back, handed me a slip of paper with my card and said, "Go to the address on this paper and ask for Hauptman. He wants you to start right away."

I thanked him and went outside. While I was reading the paper to find out where to go, a little guy with a big snoz came out and asked, "Are you going to the tannery too?"

"I don't know," I said. "All it says on the slip is Goodman and Sons and the address."

"Then you're going the same place as me. Goodman and Sons is a tannery. We can walk—it's only about four blocks." His big teeth gleamed when he grinned.

On the way we speculated about what kind of job we'd get. "Being a tannery," I said, "it's not likely to be a shoveling job, but I don't mind if it is. Using a banjo gives you a lot of time to dream. I remember one time in Montana. I was working in a ditch with a guy we called Crapper, because he spent most of the day in the bush having a railroad crap. He was either going in or coming out."

"What's a railroad crap?" the little guy asked.

"That's when a guy takes three or four times longer to crap than he needs to. While he's shitting he's not working. But getting back to the story, Crapper never put much dirt on his shovel when he shoveled. The foreman came along one day and stood above the ditch watching us. The Crapper was swinging his shovel to beat hell to show the boss what a good worker he was But the foreman jumped into the ditch, tapped Crapper on the shoulder and said, 'Crapper, never mind about the front of the banjo. Fill up the back and the front will look after itself.' And he climbed out again before Crapper could think of an answer."

The little guy laughed. "That's quite a story. My name's Gene Renault." And he gave me his hand.

At the tannery, Karl Hauptman took the papers from us and asked, "Did they tell you at the office how much we pay an hour?"

I let Gene carry the ball. "No," he said, "but we'd like to know."

"Fifty cents an hour, eight hours a day, six days a week. You get paid every Friday, and we don't give draws," he said. He stopped a passing worker who was pushing a two-wheeled truck. "Put that truck away for a little while, Walter. Take these men and get them started spreading hides. Get them some gear and show them where to change. Then show them what to do and stay with them until they can do it well enough there'll be no foul-ups." And Hauptman took off.

"Wait here till I ditch this truck," said Walter. "I'll be back and get you outfitted."

When he came back he took us to a dank but brightly lit room. There was a bench along one wall, with large hooks fastened above it. Hanging from each hook were a pair of waterproof cotton pants and a long bibbed apron. Beneath the bench stood a row of knee-length rubber boots.

"You better change your pants for a pair of those waterproofs and put on an apron. And find a pair of rubber boots that fit. The job you're gonna do ain't hard, but it's goddamn messy and stinks a bit. You can wash the stink off yourself but not your clothes."

Then he pointed to a frame partition running halfway across the room. "Hang your duds on that wall over there. There's showers behind it, so you can leave here smelling like roses. Right now there's a couple of things I have to see to, but I'll be back by the time you get changed."

The part of the plant Walter took us to was where the hides were being unloaded from trucks. They came off the trucks folded and varied in weight. Most were from forty-five to eighty pounds. Bulls weighed as much as a hundred and fifteen pounds, but there weren't many of them. Our job was to unfold the hides, spread them out and sprinkle salt on them.

We piled them in rows, the hair side down, then salted them

192

liberally. Each row ran the width of the building. To make the rows three feet high we used a system that created steps. When the back row was two feet high, we made a row a foot high in front of it, and worked off it to pile another foot of hides on the back row.

It took Walter only fifteen minutes to show us the ropes. Then he took off, saying, "You won't have any trouble. There's fuck-all to learn. Just make sure you salt them the way I showed you."

"He's right!" Gene said. "All you need to do this job is a strong back and a weak mind and a beak that can't smell. I got the first two, but this big horn of mine is working like it was on bonus. What a fucking stink. I don't think I'll be around very long."

"You'll get used to it," I said. "In a couple of days, if we're here that long, you won't notice it. I'd like to get the hell out, too, but I need the money. So I'll stick it out if the job lasts, but I might have to drag up if I can't get a draw, and Hauptman says there's no draws. I only got two bucks in my kick and that'll only see me through tomorrow."

Gene was good people and a hard worker. We worked well together without much gab, but the morning went fast and the stink became bearable.

Walter came back at five minutes to twelve. "Everything going okay?" he asked. "Looks like you're doing a good job. At least you're keeping up to Mario—that's the fellow bringing you the hides. If you don't know where the washroom is, I'll show you. It's a little early to knock off, but come with me anyhow. There's a good place to eat across the street. You can get a brew with your meal, 'cause the cops are taken care of, and you don't have to change. A lot of the guys eat there. It's cheap and the food's good."

We stopped work and followed him. After we washed we took off for the hash house and had a good feed. They served the beer in gallon and half-gallon tin pails with a big head on it. Two guys drinking together would drink out of the same half-gallon pail. More than two would order a gallon bucket.

Gene and I were finished scoffing and were nursing a can when he said, "Maybe I can help you out, and you won't have to quit. The boardinghouse where I live is run by a widow about fifty-five years old. Three other guys and me have been staying there for over two years 'cause the food is good and she packs a good lunch. The rooms are clean, and she only charges eight dollars a week. There's a vacant room for two more boarders. I'll ask her to carry you until you get paid. You can come with me when we finish work. It's within walking distance from here. I'm pretty sure she will, because she's did it before."

"Thanks," I said. "That would be a hell of a good deal for me if you can swing it."

Hauptman must have put Walter somewhere else to work, for we never saw him in the afternoon. At four-thirty, Hauptman came and watched us for five minutes before telling us to go to the office and get time cards. "That'll take a few minutes. Knock off when I leave. Then go have a shower and change before you go. Those assholes in the office got tender noses and would be too goddamn busy holding them with handkerchiefs to look after you. The whistle blows at eight in the morning. Be changed and ready to start by then. I'll okay a nine o'clock start this morning. That should make you happy, seeing as how it was after ten when you got here."

Hoping I could con Gene's landlady into putting me on the cuff until payday I went with him to his boardinghouse. It was an old but well-kept brick building with a dormered slate roof.

Mrs. Crawford was a tall, slender, raw-boned woman. "I'll go along with you, Gene," she said. "If you think your friend is worth a trust, I'll take a gamble." She turned to me. "May I call you Legs, like Gene does? All my boarders call me Janis, and I call them by their first names. Anyway, while I set another place at the table, let Gene show you your room. You can take your pick of either bed."

We went upstairs. Gene opened the bedroom door, and said, "This is it. The rooms are large but the closets are small. If you're like me, though, you don't have much to stash in them anyway."

"That's for sure! I'm standing in every goddamn rag I own."

"There's a couple of things I oughta tell you about this place. You have the use of the parlor and dining room. There's a radio in the parlor. Everybody can use it, but don't play it too loud. All of us, even Janis, listen to "Amos 'n' Andy" after supper. You can use the phone in the hall, but Janis don't like it if you get too many calls. Between meals the icebox is open to everybody, but be sure and clean up any mess you make or you'll hear about it from her."

"Sounds like you guys got it made. No goddamn wonder you've been here so long. The way you tell it, it's going to take a guy with a shotgun to get me out of here."

Janis set a good table. It was pitch till you win. She put all the main dishes on the table. There was a mountain of pork chops on a big platter, heaping bowls of vegetables, two bowls of rich gravy, homemade bread and home-baked pies for dessert.

I was about to reach for the pork chops when Janis came from the kitchen and took the chair at the head of the table. When she sat down I had my arm out again, but I saw the guys on the other side of the table bowing their heads and I jerked it back. They were waiting for Janis to give thanks. The grace was short, and when it was over everyone took his best lick. The only conversation at the table was, "Please pass" this or that and "Thank you," except when Janis introduced me to the other boarders. No one left the table until the pie was finished. Then everyone waited for Janis to rise before heading into the parlor. Janis busied herself clearing the table until the news was over and "Amos 'n' Andy" came on. Then she joined us.

When the program was over I went to my room and lay on the bed putting the figures on the day's happenings. The job was piss poor and stank, but if I kept it I could stay in St. Louis. Did I want to stay in St. Louis? Big cities gave me a pain in the ass. I hated them. Everyone rushing around like autumn leaves in a windstorm. The open country was the only place I could be content. It didn't matter whether I was swinging a spike maul or driving a four-up hauling freight in the bush, the air was clean.

Facing the facts head on, Nancy Evans was a beautiful woman and the only reason I took the job and stayed in St. Louis. Was this good enough? Our feelings were lust, not love. Was a tumble in bed a few times a week with another man's wife worth staying on a job I detested? I was committed to Janis for a week's board and room. Her boardinghouse was the only place I'd lived that felt like home since my mother died. I would stay long enough to see Nancy again and keep my commitment to Mrs. Crawford.

Gene and the other boarders were at the dining table playing euchre when I came downstairs. They were playing for blood, not money, and the game was spirited. I stood and watched until I heard the living-room clock chime eight. Tired of kibitzing, I went to the hall to get my coat and go outside. Where to? I didn't know, but I didn't give a damn, as long as it was outside. Between the employment office, the job and the boardinghouse, I'd been cooped up all day. I went to the phone and was going to phone Nancy to tell her I had a job and would be around for a while, but changed my mind. The hall door was open and I didn't want four guys on the eary to hear my conversation.

I walked four blocks before I stopped at a cigar store and bought a sack of Duke's Mixture and a package of wheat-straw papers. There was a public phone at the rear of the store. I fished out the piece of paper with Nancy's phone number on it and called her.

The phone rang six times and I was about to hang up when a woman answered, "Hello?"

"Nancy?" I said.

"Oh! Hello! You haven't left town after all. When I didn't hear, I was sure you'd gone. Did you get a job?"

"Yes, I did," I replied. "I don't like it much, but it's a living for the time being."

"When am I going to see you? Are you coming out tonight?"

"Not tonight. I have to line up a boardinghouse," I lied.

"What's the matter with spending the night here? You could find a place tomorrow. I've been thinking about you all day. Last night I lay awake until two o'clock hoping I'd see you again. Why is it so important to find a boardinghouse tonight?"

"I'll tell you why. I don't mind screwing another man's wife, but I don't want to sleep in his bed. I'll see you after dark tomorrow, when there's less chance the neighbors will see me coming and going," I answered tartly. I was getting hard, and if I kept talking I knew I'd wind up there.

"Oh, God," she moaned. "I can see I'm going to be awake all

night again thinking about tomorrow."

"You're not the only one who's going to be thinking about it all night. But I've got to hang up. I'm calling from a public phone and there's a woman waiting to use it. I don't like people listening to me when I'm talking to my best girl. See you tomorrow."

I got Boots's number from the hospital switchboard. When I dialed it there was no answer. I hung up and dialed again; still no answer. I weakened and started dialing Nancy's number again, then slammed the receiver back on the hook, picked the jit out of the return slot and returned to the boarding house. Gene and his buddies were still playing cards and Mrs. Crawford was listening to the radio. I went in and sat on the sofa.

When the commercial came on Janis asked me if I'd got my clothes. "I'm wearing them," I answered. "These are all the clothes I have. I'll cure that when I get a few dollars to spare. I sure could use a clean shirt and underwear."

"Why don't you wash them tonight, and they'll be dry by morning? Gene and the boys do their own laundry most of the time." She turned off the radio and took me to the basement where two concrete laundry tubs were fastened to the wall. "There's soap on the shelf and a clothesline by the furnace. If you wring them out good, they'll be dry in no time."

I followed her back upstairs, went to my room and peeled off my shirt, socks and underwear. Then, in just my pants, shoes and frayed cardigan, I returned to the basement and started to scrub.

In the morning I went to the basement and changed behind the furnace before breakfast.

I met Mrs. Crawford in the hallway. "The biscuits will be ready in ten minutes," she said. "Shall I pack a lunch for you? I'm packing one for Gene."

"Yes, please," I said. "If you're packing one for Gene I'll take one too."

Breakfast was on a par with supper: ham, eggs, grits, hot biscuits and all the coffee you could drink.

On the way to work I told Gene, "Tomorrow's the big day for us, buddy—Friday! The day the eagle shits. Eleven hard ones and a half a rock the way I figure it. What you going to do with a bundle of scratch like that? I won't even have walking-around money if I pay Janis what I owe her and a week's advance."

"She's a good woman. She won't even expect you to if she knows it'll clean you out. Just tell her like it is. I often borrow a few bucks from her if I go on a bender and wind up broke."

Most of the working stiffs ate their lunch beside their work or in the washroom, but Gene and I went outside. It was nippy, but the sun was shining and there was no stink. Gene had a thermos in his lunchbox and wanted to share his coffee with me, but I refused. "On a cold day like this you can use it all yourself. I'll scoff, then get a coffee across the street."

"Then we'll split this and both get a coffee or beer," he urged.

Ten minutes later we were in the hash house, passing a beer back and forth. "You know," said Gene, "it's like you said. I don't notice the stink so much today. I once knew a night owl, and I asked how he could stand the smell of the honey wagon. He told me, 'The first week was a tough one. After the second week you forget about it. I never even get off the seat of the honey wagon to eat any more. And I wouldn't want another job. The money's good, and you never see the boss because he can't stand the smell.' I wouldn't want that to happen to me. I'd hate to spend the rest of my life salting hides, but I guess there's not much danger of that happening. I've lost every job I ever had through booze, and I've had some good ones."

"At least you know your problem," I said. "I wish to Christ I knew mine. Every job I've ever had I got fed up with and quit. I know goddamn well I won't keep this job very long. As soon as I get over being pussy struck I'll be long gone, and another job and town will go down the drain."

After supper I got Boots on the phone. He knew my voice at once.

"Legs, ya old son of a bitch! Where ya calling from? You never left town, you bastard. I'm off Sunday. Ya gonna still be in town? Tell me, what happened that you're still here?"

"I will if you'll clam up long enough. I took a job in a tannery and I'll tell you why on Sunday if we get together. How's the job working out?"

"Aces," he said enthusiastically. "It's a hell of a good deal. The Joe I'm helping's real good people. He's got me studying. Where'll I meet you Sunday?"

"I'll come out there, if they allow visitors," I said.

"Sure. They'll even feed ya if you're here in time for dinner."

"Good. I'll wait in the admitting lobby."

It was eight-thirty when I got to Nancy's. This time I went to the front door. When it closed she threw her arms around me, found my mouth with hers and gave me a long hot kiss like I never had before. That's one part of lovemaking I didn't know anything about, but she was a good teacher, and I was a fast learner. We stayed in a clutch for a long time before backing off.

For the first time I saw her fully made up, wearing a dress and high heels. She was dazzling, with her waved blonde hair tucked behind her ears, and her wide, sky-blue eyes shadowed with a tinge of azure. She pursed her red lips and said, "You like it? I spent all afternoon getting primped up for you."

"Like it! You look like a goddess. The tramp and the goddess. That's a combination. It would make a good name for a book."

"Don't be so hard on yourself. You don't know how handsome you are. Even those clothes you're wearing can't hide that. And with them off you're really something to look at." Our lips met again.

She led me to the sofa in the front room. "Tell me all about your job and how you got it."

"I got it through the government employment office. The job is horseshit. It's not worth talking about. I'm salting hides in a tannery. The only reason I'm keeping it is you," I said.

"You couldn't have said anything nicer. Don't talk about the job if it bothers you." She put her arms around me, stretched out on the sofa, pulling me down with her, and gave me more lessons in foreplay.

This was new to me, and I went for it in a big way. In fact, I gave her a jump on the sofa with all her clothes on except her pants and high heels. After we washed up we left the bathroom naked and went to bed. We made love twice more before midnight. She gave me a hard time when I finally said I was leaving, but I got dressed anyway. "If all goes well," I said, "I'll see you Monday."

There were no buses running at that hour, and it took me over an hour to walk home. On the way, guilt caught up to me again. Fear of being caught with my jeans down didn't bother me, but the feeling I was siphoning gas out of the man's car did.

There was no sleep for the first hour after I crawled between the sheets. Then I was afraid if I went to sleep I'd sleep in. I tried to stay awake, but the old man with the sand caught up to me.

When I came to, Gene was shaking hell out of me. As I opened my eyes he said, "By Jesus, Legs, you're a hard man to wake. I thought you were dead. You still got time to make the table if you fan your ass. You can't miss today's shift or you'll have to wait till Monday for your pay."

Still half asleep, I staggered to the bathroom in my underwear and put myself in high gear by sticking my kisser in cold water. I just made the table in time for grace.

It was a long rough day for me. I spent more time looking at the clock on the wall than I did salting hides, but by then we both knew all the angles of the job and either one of us could have done it alone. Walter came by before quitting time and I asked him if we got paid by check or cash.

"Check," he said. "You'll see the lineup when you're punching out. Don't worry about getting it cashed. All it will cost you is the price of a beer across the street. Everybody goes there, and some of them are still there when the joint closes."

We went all out when we cashed our checks, and had two cans of beer before heading home for supper. Mrs. Crawford wouldn't take the twelve dollars I offered her. "How much does that leave you with?" she asked.

"As much as I had the first night I came."

"Then give me seven dollars and keep five. You must need a few things for yourself. You can catch up next payday."

I thanked her and gave her the seven big ones, put the fin in my pocket, went to the parlor and turned on the radio. Gene and one of the boarders came in and we chinned until supper. Afterwards,

I took off for the skid row to get a pair of second-hand strides and low-cuts because I didn't like lounging around Mrs. Crawford's in my big logging boots. I had a deuce left when I paid for the strides and kicks, so I sprang for a pair of two-bit socks before going home to catch up on sleep.

Saturday morning it was pouring rain, which turned to snow before noon. Gene and I got our asses soaked walking to work, and for the first time since we hired on, we were glad to put the oilers on so we could hang our clothes up to dry. The snow stopped falling before five, but we had to slog through three inches of it to get to the boardinghouse.

It turned mild during the night, and the Sunday-morning sun coupled with a warm southern breeze melted the snow, making the late morning walk to the sanatorium pleasant. When I got there, Boots was sitting on the stone railing of the wide marble steps. He spotted me, waved and came to meet me.

"Christ, it's good to see ya. Yuh took a job, ya old bastard. You been listening to your own preaching and got work ways. Tell me what you been doing?"

"I'll tell you everything later. What time they put the nose bag on?"

"We've got lots of time. The cafeteria opens at eleven-thirty and closes at one-thirty. Come on, let's walk around the grounds."

"Well, to begin with," I said, "I met a woman. She's a married woman, about twenty-five. When I left here the other day, I was feeling pretty goddamn low. So I started walking back to the skid row instead of taking the bus, but I got hungry and put the beg on a house. And this barefoot woman, wearing only a wraparound, opened the door." I gave Boots a detailed run-through of my meeting with Nancy Evans and the tannery job.

When I finished he shook his head, grinning. "Man! Have you got it made—a steady job and a steady lay. You lucky bastard. Nothin' like that ever happens to me. Have you been back for seconds?"

"Yes, but I don't know whether I'm going back again. Somehow I don't feel right about screwing another man's wife. I feel like I'm beating him to his traps and stealing his furs."

"What ya worrying about? You never heard of a pussy wearing out did ya? Take it while you can, that's my motto."

"You got a point, but I can't help how I feel. Anyway, tell me how things are going for you? Have you got in touch with your folks yet?"

"Not yet. I want to get a few bucks ahead and buy some new duds, and be able to take my dad out for a few beers when I see him. If you've had enough walking I'll show you inside and take you to my room."

In Boots's room he showed me the books he was studying. "Christ, Legs, it's like being in school again. Sandy, that's the engineer's name, gives me tests to make sure I'm hitting the books, and all day long he's teaching me. With all his help I'm a cinch to get my papers when I get my time in."

I met Sandy, a Scot with a sense of humor, and I knew from the off-handed way he spoke to Boots that he was pleased with him. It made me feel good.

Dinner was top-drawer. There was a choice of roast beef or chicken, four kinds of vegetables, and any kind of topping you wanted. Boots heaped his plate and had pie and ice cream. I stuffed myself, but there was no way I could get around all the grub Boots did. After dinner we went to Boots's room and rehashed past experiences till nearly four. Then I took off to get back to the boardinghouse in time for Janis's Sunday supper.

I worried all day Monday about going to Nancy's and wished I hadn't given her my word I'd go. It was dark when I arrived. We smooched for twenty minutes before climbing in the tub together, and when we'd dried each other off we went to bed—but not to sleep.

At ten-thirty when I refused to listen to Nancy's pleadings to stay all night, she said, "I don't think you come out here because you want to be with me. If it weren't for sex I don't think I'd see you at all."

"You know better than that. I have to catch the bus, and it doesn't run after eleven. I'll see you Wednesday."

"Wednesday? What's the matter with Tuesday? Why can't you

come tomorrow? Or don't you like to fuck on Tuesdays?"

"I've never given you reason to talk like that," I said, "but I don't think we ought to overdo it. How do you know your neighbors haven't seen me coming and going? I told Boots I'd spend the evening with him, but I'll call him and say I can't make it, and I'll see you tomorrow after dark."

When I was dressed and ready to leave Nancy got out of bed, slipped on a kimono and came to the door to kiss me goodnight. She held me in a clinch so long I had to run to catch the bus.

She never put up a squawk when I left on Tuesday. But Wednesday when I was getting ready to tell her I was going to leave early, she beat me to the draw with, "I'm not looking forward to the weekend."

"Why?" I asked.

"I shouldn't have to tell you that. Carl will be home and I can't see you for three days."

"I don't know how to tell you this, Nancy, but to start, we got to call a halt to what we're doing. There's no future in it for you. I'm not good for you or any woman. I'm too goddamned mixed up. I'm not even good for myself, let alone a woman like you. You got everything going for you here, and you're going to blow it for a tramp like me. I'm going to leave town next Wednesday. I'd leave sooner, but I won't have enough to pay my landlady before then." When I finished talking, I was sweating like a stake horse after winning a mile-and-a-quarter stake race.

"Don't be so noble. I've been wanting to leave Carl for over a year now, but never had the guts to do it until you came along. You got a job, and I'll get one too. We don't have to have a place like this. We can live in a furnished flat until you get a better job and we get some money saved. I always worked until I married Carl, and I can do it again."

When she said this the body temperature jumped another twenty degrees. I had to find a way out without hurting her more than I already had.

I blundered on. "There's more to it than setting up housekeeping. For two people to live together and stay happy, they have to be in love with each other. You must have loved Carl when you married him, and it didn't work out. If you couldn't make a go of it under those conditions, how long do you think we could stay together, with nothing going for us? I said from the start we were going to get burned if we kept playing with fire, even if I didn't put it in those words."

At that, she really lit into me. I'd expected a strong reaction, but even so I was surprised.

"Nothing going for us, you say? Maybe not for you. You come into my life, turn everything upside down and now you're all set to walk out just like it never happened. You say you don't love me, and when I look back, the way you've acted since the second time you came here, I knew that and accepted it. Now you want to walk out as if nothing ever happened between us. If you can walk out of here with a clear conscience, go ahead. I'll make out. You're not the first man that's walked out on me. At least I had you for a while. And you're right, I don't love you or any man. You're all the same, You're only interested in one thing." And suddenly, she began to sob.

"I'm sorry if you feel I've not been on the level with you," I said, and got out of bed.

I was putting on my shorts when she whimpered, "I know you're leaving. You made that clear, but are you in such a goddamn rush to get rid of me you got to leave now? Let's not part this way. Get back in bed. You said Wednesday; that's a week away. Let's make the most of the time left between now and then."

I kicked off my shorts, got back in bed and stayed so long I had to walk home. This time I made it without a troubled mind. Nancy was more annoyed than hurt, and that gave me peace of mind.

I saw her on Thursday and Monday. Then on Tuesday, the last night we'd be together, I stayed until dawn was breaking. When we said goodbye at the door we both choked up. We spent a long time in a clinch before parting.

Friday, Gene and I cashed our checks and had two cans of beer before supper. I settled up with Mrs. Crawford and told her I was leaving town Wednesday. I offered to pay a full week's board in advance, but she wouldn't go for it. "If you're leaving Wednesday," she said, "you'll only be here for half a week. Four dollars is enough. I'm sorry you're leaving. You've been a good boarder. But I guess you have your reasons, and I'm not one to pry."

We finished supper, and everyone except Janis, who was busy with after-dinner chores, went into the parlor to listen to the radio. The nightly newscast ended, and before "Amos 'n' Andy" came on we were being bombarded with commercials. Normally by this time Janis would have joined us, but tonight a phone call had kept her late.

Without her civilizing presence, debate among the boarders could sometimes get heated. Tonight, during the commercials, one of the boarders began talking about the past world war: "There'll never be another," he said, "because America is strong enough to whip any country or alliance in the world." To prove his point he added, "The world knows the Kaiser had Britain and France licked when America came to their rescue and made short work of the Huns."

Everybody nodded agreement, and one said: "No question about that. We kicked the shit out of the Germans in a hurry once our troops got there. America has never lost a war since the Declaration of Independence."

While living in Canada, Canadians display little or no nationalism, but when living in foreign countries they like to flap their own flag. Canada was part of the North American continent, and I felt U.S. citizens had no more right to call their country America without qualifying it than Canadians had. I believed the only people entitled to call themselves Americans were native Indians. I also knew the guy was wrong that the U.S. had never lost a war. I was about to blurt out, "You don't know your history very well. Canada and a small band of loyal Indians kicked shit out of the United States in 1812." But I remembered in time that Janis wouldn't thank me for starting an uproar in her living room, so I kept my trap shut.

I could see by the way Gene was fidgeting that he wasn't listening, and he left before "Amos 'n' Andy" came on. When Janis came in to listen to the show she asked, "Where's Gene?"

"You should know without asking," smirked one of the boarders. "He got paid today."

Janis scowled at him and said, "You seem to enjoy it when Gene falls off the wagon. I don't think it's anything to be smug about. It's a sickness with him. He can't help himself, and the only person he hurts is himself."

Janis was already high on my good-people list, but when she put the self-satisfied bastard in his place she zoomed to the top. The other boarders quit smiling and the subject of Gene was dropped. He was still not home when I hit the sack at eleven. At breakfast his chair was vacant, but there wasn't a single crack about his absence.

After breakfast, Janis handed me Gene's lunchbox and said, "I packed your lunch in Gene's lunch pail. He won't be needing it today. That means you'll have a thermos of coffee with your sandwiches. Poor Gene, we may not see him for a week. It all depends on how his money holds out."

"Thanks," I said. "I'll tell the foreman he's sick. If he believes me, Gene may not lose his job."

Before starting work, I went to Hauptman and told him Gene was in bed with the flu. "Everybody gets sick on Saturday," he snorted. "Do you think you can handle the work yourself? There won't be too much coming in today. The truck drivers got paid yesterday too, and a few of them'll have the flu as well. If it gets too much for you, get a-hold of Walter and tell him I said to give you a man."

It turned out Hauptman knew what he was talking about. It was a light day, and I had no trouble keeping up.

Sunday evening a cab driver came to the house. I was alone in the parlor, so I answered the door.

"I got a drunk in my cab says he lives here. Come take a look at him and see if he does. He owes me eighty cents cab fare and he's broke. If he's lying, I'm gonna turn him over to the cops."

"I guess it's Gene," I said. "Can he walk, or is he passed out? If it's him I'll pay the cab fare." I went with him and saw Gene sprawled out on the back seat, mumbling to himself and trying to get up. "It's him," I said. "Give me a hand to get him to his feet." I paid the cabby, and he helped me get Gene to the door of the house.

Everyone was surprised when Gene came to the breakfast table on Monday. I'd gotten up early, made a strong pot of coffee and taken it and two mugs to Gene's room. I had trouble getting him awake, but when I got two steaming mugs of coffee down him and coaxed him into a hot tub he started to revive. It was rough for us both, but we made it, and Janis had to pack a lunch in a bag for me.

Tuesday I told Hauptman I was pulling the pin. "I'll work tomorrow if you want me to, but I'd like to get my check when my shift's finished if you can arrange it."

"If you're leaving because you don't like the work you're doing I'd advise you to stay on. We never keep a good man on this job any longer than we have to. As soon as there's an opening in production we move him there with a raise in pay."

"I'm not leaving because I don't like the work. I'm leaving to go home and finish school," I lied.

"I'm sorry you're leaving, but glad to hear you're going back to school. Come in tomorrow and I'll see your check is ready when you clock out." He whacked me heartily on the back. "I'm sorry to lose you, son."

CHAPTER 21

STANDING BETWEEN TWO EMPTY BOXCARS IN A string of empties on a siding beside the station, I was bothered with thoughts that had never bothered me before. When was I going to stop running? Why was I leaving St. Louis? The city had been good to me, and with Hauptman's offer of a better job I could build a future. In the meantime, Mrs. Crawford's boardinghouse was like living in your own home. There was Nancy, but that was behind me whether I left St. Louis or not. I was beginning to chill on the idea of leaving when the train pulled out. If it had been ten minutes later getting under way, I would have been on my way back to Mrs. Crawford's place.

I was the only one boarded in St. Louis, but when we pulled into De Soto, two young men got on, one a tall Texan, one black. They stayed in the blind of the baggage car where I was standing, and we were packed together like subway riders at rush hour. So I climbed to the top of the water tender and sat on the toolbox behind the coal hopper. Taking the lead from me, the Texan soon climbed up and sat beside me.

"Where you bound?" he asked.

"Sunshine," I said. "I'm headed for Frisco, if something doesn't turn up to change my mind before I get there."

"I'll be with you for a few divisions then. I'm heading for Odessa, Texas. They're building a big tank farm there. It's a big dirt job, and they're going to need a lot of mule skinners. You ever work in a mud camp?"

"Odessa," I said. "That's on the Texas Pacific. Maybe I should go through Texarkana and grab the T. and P. out of there and look it over. I've never worked on a tank farm, but if they're looking for skinners I'm their man. I've worked plenty of highway and railroad camps. What kind of equipment do they use, dump wagons or fresnos?"

He said it was mostly dumps and graders. "I'm not looking to drive a four up on a fresno; I've had enough of them already. I've been thrown too goddamn often by the Johnson bar when the fresno hit a stone or a root. The last time, the bar hit me on my jaw and broke it and I was sucking soup through a straw for three weeks." He finished by suggesting I should come along with him. "I hear they're paying eighty dollars a month and found."

From what the Texan told me, I knew I was Odessa-bound, to look it over and hire on if I could. But I wanted to finish putting the figures on him before I saddled myself with him all the way there.

I pulled out my makings, filled a paper with tobacco and offered him the bag and papers. We were lighting up when the whistle of the big road hog started bellowing like a moose in rutting season, and the train began to slow down. By the time the train stopped at the junction, where the short spur line going to Potosi meets the main line, we were lying down out of sight on the tender. While we were lying there we heard someone say "Come on, you black bastard, get the hell off this train." Then the conductor poked his head over the tender deck and said, "All right, you goddamn tramps, this is the end of the line. Get off this train and stay off."

When we hit the cinders the Texan said, "The rotten son of a bitch. It wasn't costing him anything to let us ride. We'll have to walk all the way to Potosi to get a place to sleep."

"Fuck that," I said. "You go ahead and walk to Potosi if you want to. I'm taking this train out of here. That conductor's not leaving me stranded in this goddamn wilderness." I left the right of way and ran to a row of boxcars ahead of the engine and waited. When the train pulled out I boarded it, only to find that the black guy had beaten me aboard.

We climbed to the top of the tender and sat on the toolbox. The black guy had a lump he'd bummed in De Soto, three ham sandwiches and two cookies. He offered to share them with me, but I wasn't hungry and I only took a cookie. The way he gulped down the sandwiches I knew he was ravenous. A few minutes later we stopped at Ironton, and the conductor put the roust to us again. He could have saved himself the trouble, because when the train pulled out we boarded it again.

Sitting on the toolbox we rolled a smoke and started gabbing.

Mostly the black guy. He was a good talker and I listened. He was an able-bodied seaman and had traveled around the world. He was on his way to Galveston, Texas, to his ship, he said. It had laid up there for repairs and he'd gone to St. Louis to see an old girlfriend. But it turned out she had a new boyfriend, and before he was supposed to leave they put knock-out drops in his drink and took off with everything he had—with his return ticket in his wallet, along with his A.B. card. All they left him was the suit and pea jacket he was wearing. His ship was due to sail in four days and he had to get there before then or lose his berth. He got a map from a service station and tried the thumb, but it took him all afternoon to reach De Soto.

He enjoyed telling about the things he'd done in different ports of the world. Time passed quickly and soon we were slowing down and the hogger was ringing the bell for Poplar Bluff. The young Negro stopped in the middle of a story, made for the tender's ladder and said, "This is a big town. There'll be bulls here. We better not ride too far in."

He was halfway down the ladder before I followed. The train was going too fast for me to leave it, but he made it, and I watched until he disappeared in the dark.

The conductor must have wired ahead to say we were on the train, because when I dropped off the bull was waiting. He stepped out from between a string of gondolas and shouted, "Come here, you son of a bitch!"

The area was dimly lit by sparsely placed lights, and he was in the shadow of the gondolas. I was going to bolt when I saw a faint gleam beside his hip and figured it was bouncing off the barrel of a nickel-plated six-gun so I stayed where I was and let him come. He holstered his gun and said, "You're pretty goddamn cocky for your age. How many times you have to be told to stay off a train? Where's that goddamn nigger was with you? How long have you and him been together?"

"We're not together. I got on the train in St. Louis, and he and another man got on at De Soto," I answered.

"Well, where's the son of a bitch now? I'll teach that black bastard when a white man tells him to do something he better goddamn well do it. I'll get the prick when he tries to leave town."

I thought, if you knew how fast that man can run, you'd be fanning your ass up front now and ride the blind until the train gets going too fast for him to catch it. I knew the seaman was probably up front now, or soon would be, and would board the train when it pulled out. And be long gone before the copper smartened up.

"He got off well back of here. The train was going too fast for me to get off, but it didn't trouble him. He was heading up town, running away from the yards," I lied.

"He's gotta leave some time. Right now, you're the man I'm interested in. Why did you keep getting back on the train? You must have known this was going to happen. What the hell's your rush? You don't look like a boy that has any place to go to that can't wait. There's only one way anybody can ride passenger trains on this line, and that's with a ticket. Anybody caught riding without one goes to work for the county for thirty days because I take them in and lay trespassing charges against them."

"Maybe that would be the best thing that could happen to me," I said, "or it could be the worst. That would depend on whether the county would give me treatment or not."

"What kind of treatment? You look healthy enough to me. What do you need treatment for? The judge'll treat you fair, but more'n likely you'll get thirty days, and that's what you deserve."

I told him I'd learned I needed treatment when I was a waiter in Chicago. "They have a law in Chicago that says everyone serving or preparing food must take a health test every so often. I failed the Wasserman test and lost my job. I spent all my money on treatments and I'm almost cured, but the doctor said I should go to Hot Springs, Arkansas, and take the baths and the rest of my 606 shots. If I go to jail it will undo most of the treatment I've had up to now."

The bull bought my story. "In my job I have to be hard. If I listen to every sob story I hear I wouldn't be able to keep this job, but every now and then I get a soft spot, and I guess you caught me at one of those times. You're lucky I got kids of my own your age. That's why I'm not going to run you in. As a matter of fact, If you're hungry I'll buy you a meal at the Harvey House. But there's one thing I won't do. I won't let you ride no passenger out of here."

There was only a night cook on duty. He was in the kitchen. The cop pointed to the counter and said, "I'm going to the kitchen and see what the chef can rustle up."

I took a stool at the counter and waited for the cop to return, but he stayed in the kitchen until the cook came out with a stack of hot cakes, sausages, and eggs. Then the cook drew coffee for me and the bull.

The bull took a stool beside me and spooned three spoonfuls of sugar into his mug, before he said, "When you get outside that meal I'll take you to the stave mill and you can sleep there. The man on nights is a friend of mine. I'll get him to wake you at four-thirty. There's a freight train leaving here at five in the morning. If you take it and stay with it you'll get to Hot Springs in plenty of time. There's no need for you to ride passenger trains. The freights will take you any place they will. It just takes a little longer."

I fielded questions during the meal and the walk to the stave mill. I must have come across okay, because when we found the man at the mill the bull said, "Hank, this young fellow needs a place for a few hours' sleep. There's a drag leaving here around five in the morning. Wake him in time to catch it."

"Sure thing, Bert. How's everything going with you? The wife tells me you're going to be a grandfather come fall. Must be most a year now since Ellie Mae married that Peters boy."

I walked across the room and stood by the wall out of hearing, while they gabbed. Finally Bert, the yard bull, gave me a farewell wave and a final warning. "Don't forget what I said about them passenger trains."

Hank took me to a catwalk above the boilers and said, "It's going to be hard sleeping on this grating, but I reckon you're used to sleeping on hard floors so it shouldn't bother you too much. At least you'll be warm. Bert tells me you're in a rush to get to Hot Springs, Arkansas. I'll get you up in plenty of time for the train."

I thanked him and clammed up. I didn't want to play the question-and-answer game again. When he left I peeled my coat off and rolled it up for a pillow, but the grate was hard on my bones. Mrs. Crawford's good beds and white sheets had made me soft. Another month at her place and I'd be spoiled for the road. I lay there trying to put the figures on the yard bull and the two sides of his character. He accepted my bullshit story with compassion and kindness, but what would his reaction to it have been if my skin was black? What was it that warped a good man's reasoning and caused him to have so much hate for a human being he didn't even know?

I was still puzzled by the bull and people like him when I fell asleep. Then Hank was shaking me. "Son, it's four-thirty. I've just made a pot of coffee. You'll have time to wash up and have a cup or two before your train leaves. You can catch it from here. The grade is so steep it takes a long time for it to get rolling good. It's just crawling when it goes by."

"Thanks," I said. "The way I was pounding my ear, I don't think I'd have come to until tomorrow." I got groggily to my feet, picked up my coat and followed him down the ladder.

He filled a wooden bucket with water, put a steam hose in it and turned the steam on. "How hot do you want it?" he asked, and stuck a finger in the water to test it.

There was a bar of soap in a tobacco tin on the bench beside the wall; over it hung a towel. Hank put the steaming bucket on the bench. "She's all yours. You got plenty of time to shave. How do you take your coffee? Milk and sugar?"

"Just milk, please. How do you get to the can from here?"

He told me, and when I came back I had a good wash, shaved the fuzz off my kisser and was finishing the cup of coffee when I heard the highball. I gulped the last drop, put the cup on the bench and stood up to thank Hank, but he filled the cup again. "You've got lots of time. Have another coffee before you leave. It may be a long time before you get another. It'll be five minutes before the engine gets here, and ten more before the train gets past."

About thirty miles south of Poplar Bluff, we stopped at Knobel to pick up some loads, and at Swifton we took the hole for a meet, but were highballing again in half an hour. While we were in the hole, the head-end shack passed the empty I was riding in. I asked him how long we would be waiting and if there was any place nearby I could get something to eat. He told me there wasn't but that I could eat at Newport. "We should be stopping there for at least an hour, and if all goes well we should be there by eleven or soon after."

The sun was hot and at the top of the sky when we got to Newport. I hopped off the train as we entered the yards and went to a café where I loaded up on beef stew. Then I walked a few hundred yards down the track and sunned myself while waiting for the train to pull out.

From where I was lying I could see the bull prowling around the yards and it set me thinking about railroad cops. They all put up a big front and made threats, but they seldom arrested bos for trespassing. They were mostly content to kick them out of the yard with a stiff warning and threats. They knew the hobos were booming working stiffs. The growing West needed their skills and labor, and freights were their only means of transportation. However, as in all occupations, there were misfits among the railroad cops. These were the bullies and sadists who used their authority to beat and maim hobos they nabbed.

The old-timers and experienced boomers knew about these misplaced clowns, and tales of their vicious acts were embellished and told in every jungle from coast to coast. But in time the sadistic bastards would make a mistake and work over some vengeful boomer with a memory. From then on—though he might not know it—the bull lived on borrowed time. Months or weeks later the bull's corpse would be found in the yards with a boxcar coupling pin rammed up his ass.

It brought to mind a thumping I got from a bull in De Queen, Arkansas. I was beating my way on the Kansas City Southern from Shreveport, Louisiana, to the oil boom at Seminole, Oklahoma, in early January. I was warmly enough dressed for Louisiana, but not for the cold wave I ran into in Arkansas. To compound my discomfort there were no empties in the train, and I had to ride on the running board of an oil tanker. It was bearable while the sun was shining, but when it sank below the horizon the cold got me. I hung tough until the train reached De Queen, and by then I was chilled to the bone.

Dempster, the bull in De Queen, was known to be the meanest son of a bitch in the south. He had even shot and killed two defenceless hobos. To avoid the bastard I unloaded from the train before the tanker I was riding entered the yards. On the west side of the tracks not far from where I hopped off the train there was a stave mill. I knew from the jungle grapevine that the engineer working the graveyard shift was a right guy and would let me flop on the catwalk above the boiler and wake me up in time to bypass the yards so I could catch an early-morning freight up the tracks.

When the engineer shook me awake it was dark, but by the time I washed and had a coffee day was breaking. I was sure Dempster would still be in the sheets this time of the morning, but as a precaution I avoided the yards and walked north on a parallel road.

A farmer and his son were cutting and burning brush on the other side of the right-of-way, well beyond the yards. There was still no heat from the rising sun, so I crossed the track and squatted beside the fire to wait for the train. In a short while the fire attracted two other hobos. They too had given the yards a wide berth, and each had bummed a lump at the houses of early risers. They shared the lumps with me, and we were still munching on the dry fare when we heard the highball.

From where we were squatted we could see the hogger take slack and hear the clatter of the engaging couplings as the cars lurched ahead. There was no need to leave the fire until the engine was well past, since the hogger was battling a steep grade and the train was going very slowly. By the time the big road hog reached us it was winning the battle, but the hogger still poured sand, and the tallow pot had the blower on, causing the smokestack to belch black clouds of cinder-laden smoke.

We knew we were in for a cold ride when we saw the long tank train with only four loaded boxcars at the head end. We boarded a tanker in the middle of the train, went to the sunny side and were just about to sit down when we spotted Dempster working back from the head end.

When we saw him heading our way, the smallest of the two hobos, a guy named Alex, said, "Look at the big dick. You'd think his life depended on keeping tramps from riding the Kansas City Southern."

His partner, Russ, said, "Maybe so, but don't let the big son of a whore get his hands on you or he'll tear you apart like an ape shredding a coconut."

I held my tongue and concentrated on how I could outsmart the bull. I waited until Dempster was a car and a half away before I leapt off the train and ran hell-bent for the bush, running diagonally to keep abreast of the train. Alex and Russ hit the ground, too, and made a beeline for the bush with Dempster on their tail blasting away with his six-gun. I stopped when I heard the first shot and watched the chase. Dempster was firing in the air, hoping to frighten Alex and Russ and stop their flight, but the shots had the opposite effect on the fleeing hobos. Instead of stopping they ran faster. By the time they vanished in the bush, Dempster's gun was empty and he was losing ground.

When the hobos and the cop disappeared I legged it back to the train, climbed aboard, and hurried to the other side to be out of Dempster's sight, hoping he hadn't seen me double back. I rolled a smoke and sat down on the running board thinking how easy Dempster had been to outsmart. But when I looked toward the rear of the train my ego got a kick in the ass. The big prick with ears was only about eight tankers away and closing in fast. He was so sure of his quarry he didn't even come from the other side where I couldn't see him. I kept my seat on the running board until he reached my car, then I got up and went to the front of the tank, crossed over and doubled back. But Dempster had ducked out of sight at the other end, waiting for me to go by.

I didn't see him do this, but it was an even money bet he would, so I played it cagey. I stopped when I was ten feet from the end of the tank and waited for him to appear at one end or the other of the car. When he didn't show up I knew where he was, and rather than play tag with the bastard all the way to Howe, Oklahoma, I jumped off the train. When he followed, I hightailed it for the bush with him at my prat.

I outdistanced him, and by the time I came to a shallow creek I could no longer hear him crashing through the brush and thought he'd given up. But as a precaution I ran parallel to the stream until I came to a zigzag fence running through it. I crossed the stream on the fence and went two hundred yards deeper into the bush before I turned toward De Queen. Then I walked about a quarter of a mile before swinging back to the creek looking for a place to cross.

Finally I came to a place where the large branches of the willow trees bordering the stream interlocked. I was about to shinny up a tree and crawl across a branch to the other side when my skin crawled. "I got you now, you son of a bitch! Turn around and do it slow, or I'll pump you full of lead."

I froze with my arm around the tree and was about to bolt when common sense prevailed and I turned to face my pursuer. The bore of the gun barrel had a hypnotic effect; it looked to be ten inches in diameter.

"One false move," he growled, "and you're a dead man. I've done all the running I'm going to do. So get your ass over here and be quick about it."

"Okay," I said, "but I'll come across on the branches."

Dempster waved the gun and roared, "The hell you will. You'll come through the water or I'll drop you where you're standing."

"Not me. It's still frozen. I'm not going to freeze my ass off when there's no need for it. Anyway, I don't have anywhere to dry my clothes."

"I've had all the shit I'm gonna take from a smart-assed punk like you. If you're not in the water by the time I count three, I'll blow your goddamn head off," yelled the furious bull.

He started a slow count, and before he got to two I said, "I believe you're enough of a rat son of a bitch to enjoy shooting a man in cold blood, so fire away, because I'm not going to wade across."

He answered by jumping into the belly-deep creek and wading across while I stood on the bank, riveted by fear. On the way up the bank he picked up a four-foot branch about two inches thick and used it to knock me down. The blow would have killed me if I hadn't been quick enough to cover my head with my arms. Fortunately, I was able to ward off most of the blows that followed, too.

Finally he stopped and growled, "So I'm a rat son of a bitch, am I? Get on your feet, you hobo bastard. When I'm through with you, you'll know you can't flout authority and get away with it. You're gonna get a lesson you won't forget if you live to be a hundred." Cursing the big son of a bitch under my breath, I staggered to my feet. When I faced him he spun me around, booted my ass and said, "Get moving."

We walked south along the creek. Every two steps I took, he kicked me. Finally we came to a deadfall that spanned the stream and crossed to the other side. Soon we came out of the bush at the right-of-way about twenty feet above the tracks. Alex and Russ were sitting on the bank near the bush on the other side of the cut. I couldn't tell whether they enjoyed watching the bull put the boots to me or not, but Dempster said, "I'll wipe the grin off their mugs when we get a little closer."

They were still sitting on the bank when we reached the middle of the tracks, and Dempster made his move. He levelled his long-barreled pistol at the two hobos and bellowed, "Come here, you hobo bastards."

Alex and Russ were instantly off their prats and running. But when Dempster let blast with his cannon he clipped off a limb above Alex's head. Alex froze and never moved until we reached him.

Dempster shifted the gun to his left hand, pulled a sap from his hip pocket and said, "Seems like you and your buddy got no respect for the law, but you're about to learn a lesson. And seeing as how your pal's not here to get one too, I'll give you a little extra schooling. Maybe when your mate sees the results of my teaching, he'll smarten up."

The beating I got in the bush was mild compared to what Alex got. The sadistic copper wouldn't spoil his fun by hitting Alex hard enough to knock him out. But hard enough to close one eye, break his nose, split an ear and raise lumps on his head.

Dempster didn't arrest us. He'd had too many rumbles with the local law to risk another, and he knew he'd have to explain how Alex got so bloody and badly beaten. He showed us the highway and told us to take it—and we did.

When Dempster had gone, Alex said, "That big ape don't know it, but his days are numbered. He's living on borrowed time. His wife'll be a widow before long, because if some other boomer don't kill the son of a bitch I will."

"If you intend to kill the prick you better not nose it around," I warned. "Right now you got to get to a doctor. No matter what the bastard says, you can't leave town in the shape you're in. I'll go with you and find a doc to fix you up."

"Thanks, but there's no need for you to take me. Russ'll come out of hiding as soon as that big prick gets out of sight," Alex said.

Russ came out of the bush while we were talking, so I said goodbye and left. I walked at least two miles before a farmer came by in a Model-T Ford and picked me up. He was a good Joe; the only question he asked was how far I was going.

I told him what happened in De Queen and said I was going to Seminole but only wanted to go to a town with a water tank where the trains would stop, so I could catch a freight.

"If it's a place to catch a train you're looking for, you don't need to go no further'n my place. There's a long hill on a curve where a train can't go more'n ten miles an hour. Every night just after sunset there's a train goes by. I'll take you home. The wife'll fix you something to eat, and you can give me a hand to put a wagon box on its trucks. It's a little too heavy for me to do it alone, and I don't want the wife to help because she's seven months in the family way."

Everything went the way the farmer said it would, and I arrived in Seminole two days later. When I went to the jungle I met Blackie, an old pal of mine from Nanaimo, British Columbia. Blackie was a sailor and on his way to Frisco to ship out. He talked me into going with him. A week later we were in the Phoenix jungle when the hobo grapevine brought the news. Dempster's corpse had been found in the De Queen yards. He'd been impaled with a coupling pin.

The highball brought me back to the present. It was time to catch the train. I waited until the empty I'd been riding in came in sight before I left my perch and went to catch it.

A little before four in the afternoon the train pulled into Little

Rock. I left it as it entered the yard and went into town to see if I could get any information about Odessa. There were no skinners' jobs listed and nothing on any of the boards about work in Odessa. However, I talked to a clerk in one of the offices and he confirmed what the Texan told me. This removed my doubts about the tank farm. I'd go to Odessa and forget about California.

I went to the switching tower in the yards, climbed the stairs and asked the operator when the next drag would be leaving for Texarkana.

"You just missed one. There won't be another until 6:00 a.m. tomorrow."

"Thanks," I said. "That's the one I came in on. I should have stayed with it, but I wanted to go uptown and check on what's happening in Odessa. I heard there was a big job going on and they need a lot of skinners. I didn't want to go there and find out it was just a rumor. Now I got to line up a flop for tonight."

"We don't make a habit of it, but you can sleep in the bottom of the tower and keep the fire stoked for me. I'll tell my relief you're there when he gets here, or he'll put the run on you."

Once again I thanked him. I went to see my bedchamber and spent an hour sitting on an upturned pail. I was back in Saskatchewan riding a triple-gang plow with nine horses strung out up front, three abreast. I was standing on the seat so I could see the strikeout stakes, and plowing three furrows straight enough to shoot a rifle down them. When I finished the mile-long strikeout, and looked back and saw there was not a waver in them, it caused nostalgic pangs that set me thinking. I saw the strip of moist rich earth widen every time I made a round. The furrow horses refused to be pushed or pulled from the furrow by the other horses until they reached the head ridge. Then, on their own, without any guidance from me, they would make the turn and come into the furrow dead on to keep it straight. My only chore was to kick the plow in and out of the ground at the head ridges. I wanted the satisfaction of turning over land that was mine, not John farmer's. Knowing, if I was smart enough to conquer my wanderlust, maybe I could own a farm myself. But from where I sat, it looked like the only way I could make this happen would be to marry a farmer's daughter.

Hunger brought me back to Arkansas. I stoked the fire and went uptown to eat. When I finished putting away the pork chops and was ready to leave, I decided to get a lump for the train. So on the way back to the tower I bought a bag of tobacco, a loaf of punk and two tins of sardines.

By the time the train pulled into Texarkana I had eaten most of the sardines and bread. It was one-thirty in the afternoon, and the day was perfect—no wind, only a few small clouds adrift in the sky and the sun bright and warm. A good day to boil up and get a tan while waiting for your clothes to dry. I wasn't hungry, but I was dying for a cup of coffee. So I stopped on the way to the jungle and bought a small tin of milk, a bar of soap and half a pound of coffee.

CHAPTER 22

THE TEXARKANA JUNGLE WAS IN A CLEARING BY A stream surrounded by scrub pine. The first thing I spotted when I stepped into the clearing was a five-gallon oil can with the top cut off. It was sitting on two short lengths of one-inch pipe that were resting on two flat stones. A fire crackled beneath it. I knew from the stinking smell of the steam wafting out that there were safe-crackers in the jungle. I had been in jungles before when a heavy mob boiled dynamite to skim the nitroglycerin from the top of the liquid.

Four guys were sprawled on the ground by the creek, well away from the fire because the fumes of dynamite boiling give you a pounding headache. The big one in the ten-gallon hat was gesturing with both hands, talking like a tobacco auctioneer. I couldn't hear what he was saying, but when he finished everyone roared with laughter.

Knowing they were knob-knockers, I didn't connect with them or their fire. Instead, I took a small pail and a tobacco tin from beside the fire, went to the other side of the clearing and made a fire for myself. While the fire was coming to life, I went to the creek to scour the pail and tin with sand and get some water to make coffee for myself. Before the kettle began to boil, two of the men—one a tall skinny blond in his mid-thirties wearing a pea jacket and cap, the other of medium height, also blond, but older—left the jungle, leaving a young guy about my age and the big guy with the Stetson to look after the fire.

All thoughts of boiling up and getting some sun were down the sewer. I wanted to have my coffee and get the hell out of the jungle as quick as I could. But when I was pouring myself a coffee, the young guy came over and asked, "Where did you come from?" That face! I knew that face. Where had I seen it before? My memory wasn't ringing any bells. Anyway, even if he was someone out of the past, he was a heavy man now and I didn't want any part of that mob. So I answered, "Little Rock," and clammed up.

"That coffee smells good. If I get something to drink out of, can you spare a cup?" he asked.

"Sure, get a can and take all you want. There's more than I can drink. Maybe your mate would like some?"

He got a small can and helped himself to the coffee. I handed him the milk tin. "I'm sorry I don't have sugar; I don't use it. What about your mate, isn't he drinking?"

"No. He said to say thanks, but he doesn't feel so good."

I figured he must have taken too many whiffs of steam from the boiling can. I almost made a crack about it, but held my tongue. I didn't want them to know I was hep to what they were doing.

"That's too bad. I hope it's not serious," I said.

"No, there ain't nothing wrong with him fresh air won't fix up. Where you heading from here?" he asked.

I got to my feet and said, "Odessa. There's a big construction job starting there. Do you want another coffee? If not, I'll use it to put the fire out before I leave."

He took another coffee, and while he drank it I dumped the grounds on the fire and went to the creek for a pail of water to finish dousing the fire. Then I sealed the small hole in the milk tin with a cigarette paper and, on the way out of the jungle, stashed it and the coffee in the bush.

That evening after I'd eaten and found a flop for the night, I showered and went to the pool room. The skinny guy and his pal were shooting pool with three other chaps.

I stopped and watched a couple of games before I took a seat beside the table. In half an hour the guy with the Stetson and the young guy came in. They nodded to me before sitting down to watch the game. Again, that face! It bothered me. I knew the guy, but from where? We watched several more games before the young guy asked if I wanted to play Boston. We went to a table and flipped for break. He won the flip, broke the balls and fluked the fourteen ball. The one and two balls were open and easy shots. He potted both, then missed, leaving me hooked on the trey. I blanked out when I shot and he made the three and four, hooking me again when he missed. I went to the cushion, shooting hard. I hit the five off the cushion and gave three stripes a ride, but came up empty and left him to set up again. He made the five and lucked the eight. It began to look as if he was going to take me and I'd be stuck for the game, but he missed and left me open and I ran the table.

"That's it for me," he said. "You're out of my class. Why don't you get in the Kelly game? You'd clean up. None of those guys can carry your cue. Tell me what do you answer to? My name's Gerry."

"Everybody calls me Legs," I said. "A guy in the can at the Canadian border gave me that handle two years ago, and it's stuck with me. I'd get in the game, but I'm not packing very heavy, and there's five guys playing. I'd be the last to get a shot, and if the breaks went against me I'd be wiped out before I got a chance to cash."

"I'll stake you and we'll split," offered Gerry. "You'll eat those guys. We might as well make a few easy bucks."

"You got yourself a horse," I agreed. "Who knows, I could get lucky. There's quite a lot of money in the game."

When the pool room closed at one o'clock, Gerry and I went to a café to eat and split the night's winnings, which amounted to thirty-four dollars and change. I was chomping on a steak when it hit me like a kick in the ass with an army boot. The face! I had it! Gerry, short for Gerald. He was Mrs. Cox's son from Joliet.

"Do you get Gerry because it's short for Gerald?" I asked.

"Yeah, that's right."

"And you hail from Joliet?" I asked.

"How the hell do you know that?"

I could see I shook him up. I said, "I'm psychic. I know a hell of a lot more about you, too. Your last name's Cox, and your mother works in the library at Joliet. I know why you left home, and why you should go back."

"Man! you really do know. You're scaring hell out of me with all that psychic talk. Somebody must have gave you a line on me. You couldn't have picked it out of the blue."

"You're right, somebody did," I said. "Your mother did." I told him about coming through Joliet with ten inches of snow on the ground and the temperature colder than a whore's heart. And about going to the library to get out of the cold and kill time and meeting his mother there. "Your mother knew I was on the road and gave me a cup of coffee and a sandwich. While I was eating she opened up about you. She even told me why you left home, and how badly your father and her want you to come home. She hoped if I met you I could persuade you to go back."

"Don't think I don't want to go home," he said, "because I do. But I'm not going home with the ass out of my pants, and I don't think you would either."

"Yeah, I see your point. We all have pride, even if we don't do anything to be proud about. That kind of pride is as phony as a four-dollar bill. We're losers, and we always will be until we get smart enough to kick ourselves in the ass. Your folks don't care if you come home bare-assed or decked out like a movie star. All they're interested in is getting you home and helping you make a start in the right direction."

"You're right," he said. "But it don't have to be that way. In two weeks I'll be packing a bankroll, and I can go home in style."

"I wouldn't count on it. You may be in a place you can't leave for five or six years," I said.

"What do you mean by that crack?"

"You know goddamn well what I mean. I mean you'll be in stir, that's what I mean. The way you're heading you could be a guest of Arkansas State for a few years."

Gerald bristled and said, "You're pretty goddamn smart. What makes you think I'm headed for the pen?"

"Cool down. For Christ's sake, man! You and those three knob-knockers must think I'm pretty goddamned stupid. You think I don't know what was in that oilcan on the fire? No goddamn wonder your mate didn't feel good yesterday. He got too many whiffs of the fog it gave off. I don't expect you to listen to me, but I been farther around a ham bone looking for meat than you've been away from home. I'm not running off at the mouth. I'm telling God's truth when I say you'll wind up in the big house. You may get away with it this time, but sooner or later you'll get caught."

"What are you, a preacher? A stool pigeon? For Christ's sake, lay off me! And if you've any intention of hollering copper forget it, because they'd never find the stuff where we got it planted, and if they put the snatch on any of us we're all clean. Sure, two of them have done time, but they're smarter now. They won't make the same mistake this time. I'm with a good mob. At my age, I'm lucky to be connected."

It was pretty clear to me his pals had sold him a line and he'd been sucker enough to buy it. "Who do you think you're shitting, telling me you're lucky to be in?" I said, hoping to needle him into opening his eyes. "Believe me, brother, it's on account of your age you're in, not on account of what you know. You think I don't know the big guy in the Stetson's going up your moon? You know as well as I do, or you should, if they make a clean score they're not going to split the haul with you. You'll get pieced off like a shack-up broad. I couldn't care less about that, but I do care about your mother. She's a good woman and I owe her a favor. You know goddamn well I'm no stool pigeon or I'd have sung yesterday when the cops could of caught you with the goods."

He didn't deny any of it, but just sat quietly for a while, thinking it over. Eventually he said, "Sure I'd like to go home, but it wouldn't work out. I'm not the same kid that left two years ago. I'd like to go back for a week or two, to see my mom and dad and let them know I'm doing all right. But the only way I can do that is to get some new duds and come riding in on the cushions with a few bucks in my pocket."

"You can tell me it's none of my business," I said, "but when are you and your buddies pulling this caper?"

He stared at me before answering. "The money won't be in the box for three weeks."

"Then there's lots of time to go visit your folks. I'll make a deal with you. If you agree to go home, I'll put off my trip to the coast and go to Joliet with you. You got a few bucks. If you use it and the money we won last night you can go home dressed like a banker. You can get a good second-hand suit and a pair of kicks in St. Louis for fifteen bucks. Then we'll take a freight to Elwood. You can get slicked up in your new fiddle and catch a passenger from there to

Joliet for less than half a buck, and that'll leave you with walking-around money. Nobody will know how much dough you're packing."

Gerald tossed a coin in the air and caught it as it dropped. "Call it and I'll go," he said when he'd plopped it on the table under his hand.

"Hold it! We're talking about your future. You can't let the flip of a coin call the shot on that."

"Call it," he said.

"Tails, then, if that's the way you want it. It's your life, not mine."

I expected him to hedge when he raised his hand and saw I called it right. But he smiled and said, "You win, it's tails. When do you want to leave?"

"The sooner the better," I said. "I don't want you changing your mind."

"Then let's leave this morning, because if I sleep on it I might not go. I'll go tell Barney—he's the guy with the Stetson. Our room is just across the street. Wait here, I'll be back in fifteen minutes and be ready to go."

I was sleepy and wanted to use the flop I'd paid for, but I had another coffee and waited. Cox was back before I finished sipping on it. When we went to the yards he was happier than a pig in shit and never stopped talking about what he was going to do when he got home. But the way things turned out, it would have been better if I'd used the cot in the flophouse.

We couldn't have timed it better getting to the yards. We barely had time to find an empty and board it before the train pulled out. I rolled a smoke and sat in the darkness of the doorway as the long drag crept from the siding onto the main line. But when the rear-end shack closed the gate, I threw the butt away and went to the front of the car to flatten out and get some sleep.

Gerald was still dangling his feet out the door when I dozed off, and that was the last time I saw him alive. When I came to, the boxcar was bucking like a Brahma bull. I was being bounced up and down like a bronc rider breaking a cayuse. I looked for Gerald and couldn't see him. Then the boxcar took off. It flew through the air in sudden silence, then landed with a crash on its side. Through the open door I was staring at stars. I had to jump up to grab the doorjamb, so I could pull myself up to look around. We were in a ravine. The grade of the roadbed was thirty feet above me, and there were at least twenty loads—boxcar, tankers, flats and gondolas—heaped in a giant pile. The car I was in was on top. The locomotive was out of sight and I thought it was buried in the tangle. But when I scrambled down from my perch I saw the engine upside down, belching steam, on the side of the roadbed.

There was no one in sight, but I could see two bobbing lights at the rear of the train moving toward me. I knew it was the tail-end crew coming to see what had happened. Walking to meet them I came to the hogger bending over the tallow pot, who was writhing on the ground in great pain.

"Where'd you come from?" the engineer asked.

"Texarkana. I was in that empty sitting on top of the pileup." Then, pointing to the fireman on the ground, I asked, "Don't you think we should put something over him and try to make him more comfortable?" I took my coat off and spread it over the fireman before asking the hogger for his smock to make a pillow.

He peeled it off, and when he put it under the tallow pot's head said, "I don't know how bad he's hurt. I was busy closing the throttle and dumping the fire when he jumped. I'm lucky I jumped off the same side or I'd be under that pile of wreckage. Were you alone?"

"There was another guy in the boxcar with me," I said. "The last time I saw him he was sitting in the doorway, dangling his legs out the door. He was gone when the crash woke me up. I sure hope he's all right."

"He may be all right, but it's more than likely he's under that pile of cars. We're going to have to get some help for Jake. He's stopped moaning. I guess he's in shock. When you don't know how bad a man's hurt it's dangerous to move him, in case it's his neck or back." He looked, up. "Christ, it's taking the conductor and brakeman a helluva long time getting here. Looks like those lanterns are standing still. How about you hustling back there and telling them to get the hell up here in a hurry? Tell them Jake's hurt bad and I need help."

I took off, running like a grayhound, and when I got to the three guys I gasped, "The engineer sent me to tell you to hurry. The fireman's badly hurt and needs help."

"Help?" the conductor said. "If Jake's hurt what the hell's he stopping here for? Why didn't he go on into Prescott and get him to a doctor?"

"Jesus," I said. "You mean you don't know there's been a wreck? The engine's upside down in the gully along with twenty or thirty cars."

"Oh God! I knew we came to a jolting stop, but I thought the engineer had to stop fast and jammed the air on. I didn't know it was serious." By then we were all legging it in high for the head end.

"What the fuck happened, Rube?" asked the conductor when we got there.

"I can't rightly say, but I think we spread the rails because we went quite a piece on the ties before all hell broke loose. Jake bailed out while I was closing the throttle, dumping the fire and jamming the air on," Rube said.

"Well, hell," said the conductor, "we're only a mile or so from Prescott. I'll take the young lad with me and send him back with a pushcar. The section gang keep them this side of town where they live. I'll go to the station, get the news on the wire and bring back a doctor. Arnold, you better hustle back to the crummy and get flares out. Go to the wreckage, Pete, and find something to carry Jake to the pushcar on. The kid can only bring the pushcar to where the track's torn up. You stay here with Jake, Rube, and don't try to move him until I get back with the doctor. Come on, son, let's move it."

When we got to where the pushcars were, the conductor said, "Pete may not find anything to carry Jake on. While you wrestle the car onto the tracks, I'll wake somebody up. We'll take a door off the toolshed and throw it on the car. It won't take long, and it'll be better than anything Pete will find."

The conductor was back with two section hands by the time I got the car on the rails. They stripped a door off its hinges, threw it on the car, pulled their gas car out of the shed and hooked it onto the pushcar, then pulled it to the wreck with me on it. Meanwhile, Jake had come to and was sitting up dragging on a cigarette. Rube and Pete had used wood from the wreck for splints and bound them to his broken leg with their belts and three bandanna handkerchiefs.

"It's only a broken leg and a lump on his head big as a goose egg," Rube said. "He came to a few minutes after you left. I'm glad you brought the door. It's better than what Pete found."

We carried Jake to the pushcar, and the gas car got us to the station before the doctor and ambulance arrived. But they came before the conductor got to us and said, "I see you're back with us, Jake. You in much pain?"

Jake was about to answer when the doctor nudged the conductor aside and began to examine the wounded man. He rolled his eyelids back and looked at his eyes with his ophthalmoscope, then he felt the lump on his head and asked him where else he hurt. Finally he gave Jake a shot in the arm and let the ambulance take him off.

I'd been too busy to give Gerald much thought. Now I wanted to find him. I took my coat off the pushcar and put it on. Rube said, "You've been a big help, son. I'd like to buy you breakfast. I think you earned it. Now that the ambulance has left, let's go find a café."

The conductor came to us and said, "I guess that takes care of everything here for now. The news is on the wire, and the big hook is on its way. It's going to be a while before they get this mess cleaned up and traffic moving again. There's nothing more we can do till the hook gets here, so we might as well go uptown and have breakfast."

Despite my worry about Gerald, I was ravenous enough to wolf down a big breakfast. I thanked the hogger before rushing back to the wreck.

People were swarming over the wreckage like hiving bees. There was a road within a hundred yards of the wreck that the ambulance could have used, but in the dark we didn't see it. I asked several people if any bodies had been found. One of them told me the body of a young man had been taken away half an hour before.

"Do you know where they took it?" I asked. "I knew someone

that was on the train, and he's missing now."

"I don't rightly know," he said. "I guess it was Webster's Funeral Home. It's the only one in town."

Back in town I found the funeral parlor. There was no one in the front rooms, but at the back I found the sheriff and the undertaker in a cold, high-ceiled room. Gerald's body was lying on a white porcelain-topped table in the middle of the room. The undertaker was cleaning out the corpse's pockets, and the sheriff was examining the contents.

When they heard me come in they looked up, and the undertaker asked, "Can I help you?"

I said, "No, but I think I can help you and the sheriff. I know this man's name."

"Good," the sheriff said. "Can you tell me how to get in touch with his next of kin?"

"His name is Cox, Gerald Cox. He's from Joliet, Illinois. His mother works at the library. You can reach her there. That's about all I can tell you. I only met him yesterday in Texarkana, We hopped the freight together. He was going home, I was going north. We didn't talk much, but he told me his name and where his mother worked."

"Thanks. That solves the problem, but I almost wish it didn't. Now I have to tell his mother her son is dead. I'm not very good at bringing news like that to people," said the sheriff.

When I left Gerald's body in the morgue my spirits were lower than a sunken ship. It could have been me lying on the table in there, heading for a pauper's grave. And I felt responsible for Gerald's death. Me! Mr. Do-Gooder, handing out advice to everyone, but heeding none myself. If I hadn't talked Gerald into going home, he'd still be alive. True, the kind of life he led didn't conform to society's rules, but men have been known to change. Alive there was a chance for him. Now all hope was gone.

CHAPTER 23

FUCK ODESSA AND CALIFORNIA, I THOUGHT. I'M GOING back to Canada. And I'm not hanging around here waiting for the M. and P. I'm taking the highway to where trains are moving. So I heel-and-toed it for twenty minutes before a car going my way hove in sight. When it got close I put my thumb to work. The driver hit the brakes but was going so fast it took him a hundred yards to stop. I legged it up the road, but he slammed the car into reverse and came back to pick me up.

When I opened the door of the four-door Buick, the driver said, "How far you going?"

"Canada," I answered.

"That's a hell of a big country. What part you going to?"

"Saskatchewan. I'm going back to the folks' farm."

I got in and shut the door before anything more was said. The driver was a small guy. His sharp, steel-gray eyes were set in a friendly face that put me at ease. He wore his hat tipped back, exposing a receding hairline.

He had the car rolling in the big notch before he began the usual round of questions. I parried them well. After all, I was an old hand at the game. I'd been playing it for three years. It took forty miles of probing before he figured I was a right guy. By that time I had the figures on him, but he knew fuck-all about me, except my name and that I was a Canuck.

During the probe he told me he was from the Twin Cities and his name was Eric Ericson. He was born in a farmhouse twenty-two miles from Minneapolis, but now lived and worked in the city. "If you stay with me and all goes well, I'll have you there tomorrow night."

He was queer as a four-dollar bill, but that didn't bother me. I'd had three years' experience dealing with fruits and oddballs.

Before spending the night in Kansas City, he suggested I save the price of a room by sleeping with him. I put it to him straight.

"I could use the money I'd save, but it wouldn't work very well for you. When I sleep with strange men I keep my clothes on and my fly buttoned. It'll be better for us both if I get a cheap flop and meet you here in the morning. That is, if what I've said hasn't made you change your mind about taking me the rest of the way."

"I don't know how you jumped to those conclusions," Ericson said. "But I'm not denying them. I can't help what I am any more than you can help being a bum. I'm glad you declared yourself before it got embarrassing for both of us. I'll be leaving at seven tomorrow. If you're here then, I'll take you with me."

"I'll be here, and thanks for bringing me this far, in case I sleep in. But that's not likely."

The next day he dumped me off in a Minneapolis suburb where he lived with his parents. I could have used the bus to get to the skid row, but I wanted to walk. By the time I got there on the H and T and found a flophouse it was ten-thirty. I went to a greasy spoon and put the choppers to work. Then before I flattened out for the night I asked the clerk to give me a shout at 6:00 a.m.

The following morning, I put away my bacon and eggs and was in the Great Northern yards before nine. I found out there was a drag pulling out for Minot, North Dakota, around 5:00 p.m. The weather was too cold to go to the jungle, so I went back to the skid row to find a pool room. I passed a slave market on the way and stopped to see what kind of jobs were posted. I was looking for a gandy shipment to North Dakota or Montana. I would gladly pay a deuce to ride the plush and not have to fight the cold on a freight train. I'd even go to work and hold the camp down until spring work started in Saskatchewan.

I was lucky. The Northern Pacific had two steel gangs working west of Miles City, Montana. They were replacing ninety-pound rails with heavier, hundred-and-twenty-pound steel, and needed men. The job cost a deuce and gave me a pass on the cushions to Horton, Montana, where the gang was working—an overnight run.

Two other stiffs were on the train heading for the same job. It was just past six in the morning when the conductor stopped the train at the job site. The camp—a line of railroad bunk cars and an office car on a siding—was already astir. When we went to the office car the door was open, but no one was in it. We were about to leave when the super, a wind-tanned, wide-shouldered old Swede by the name of Carl Anderson, came from his partitioned room into the office. One side of his face was shaved, the other covered with lather. He carried a razor and had a white towel draped over his shoulder.

"Good morning," he said. "Two men and a peg boy they send me. Go have your breakfast and come back. The timekeeper will be here then, and he'll get you on the payroll. Then he'll turn you over to the bull cook who'll give you some blankets and take you to your sleeping car. By that time the handcars will be leaving for work. Get on one and go to the job. The foreman or I will tell you what to do."

Anderson's crack about two men and a peg boy burned my ass. The son of a bitch was telling me I couldn't do a man's work. I almost gave him a blast and told him to shove his job up his ass, but I let it pass. A week later when I finished putting the figures on him I was glad I had.

After breakfast we climbed on one of the handcars and when we reached the job, Mike, the foreman, came over to us. He was a huge burly guy with a disfiguring purple birthmark on his left cheek that made me wonder why he didn't grow a beard.

"I need back spikers," he said. "Have any of you ever used a spike maul?"

We all said yes.

He took the other guys and said to me, "Stay here. When Carl gets around to it he'll show you what to do. He needs a peg boy."

I waited fifteen minutes watching the men at work before Carl Anderson came. The job was well organized. A gang up front was pulling spikes with claw bars. Behind them four men with lining bars were throwing the rails off the ties. It was a team effort. They would position the bars under the rail at different locations seven or eight feet apart and wait at the ready for the Yoh man to holler "Yoh!" Then they would all heave together, and the rail would fly into the ditch, pulled by the weight of the rails already in the ditch that were still connected to it.

Anderson took me to where a runty little guy was throwing the cast-iron tie plates off the ties and stacking them in piles of twelve to be picked up later. When the plates were off the rail and stacked, he poked four-inch creosote wooden pegs into the spike holes.

"Help this fellow. It's not a hard job, but one man can't keep up. He'll show you what to do."

When Anderson took off, the little guy asked, "What do they call you? I'm Jude Racine." He took off his mitt and stuck out a gnarled duke.

I shook it saying, "Legs is what I answer to."

"There ain't nothin' to learn about this job," he said. "All you gotta do is keep ahead of the guys that are driving the pegs in and smoothing off the ties with adzes. It's easy for me because the Lord built my ass so close to the ground I don't have far to bend."

"Yeah, I guess I'm a little too tall for the job," I said. "It'll be hard on my back. You don't get much time to straighten up, but I'll give it my best shot until I get a chance to get a spike maul in my hands. I like spiking, I'm good at it, but that goddamn Anderson thinks I'm too young to do a heavy job."

"Ah," Jake said, "he's got a big bark, but he's still a working Joe at heart. This is the only company he ever worked for. He started with the Northern as a water boy at fourteen. There ain't anything to do with railroad tracks he ain't done, and he knows what stiffs like you and me gotta put up with. But one thing he won't put up with is a lousy cook. I been working for him off and on for nine years and I seen a lotta cooks come and go."

By eleven my back was giving me hell, and I was glad we had to close the track for a westbound train. Everyone had to stop work while a small crew installed the switch-point that connected the new rails to the old.

Anderson took charge to make sure everything was done quickly without a hitch. When the switch-point was set to the proper gauge, four men grabbed spike mauls and spiked it to the ties. Knowing this, I had intended to be one of the grabbers, but was rolling a smoke and missed out. But I took note that none of guys spiking the point knew how to swing a spike maul, and I set my sights on making sure I grabbed a maul when we closed the track for the night.

During the day a switch-point is a safe enough connection, because flagmen caution the train to slow down and crawl past it. But at night there are no flags or flares, so you have to make a solid connection. To do this you have to cut one of the old rails to size and drill two holes in the end for the fish-plate bolts.

To cut the rail you use a cold set—a large cold chisel, with an eye in it for a wooden handle to make it safe to hold. The holder puts it on the rail and moves it slowly around as two men with mauls strike it in rhythm—like roughnecks driving stakes for a circus tent. It takes about ten minutes to cut a deep notch on all sides of the rail. This takes a lot of swinging, and the strikers tire quickly because of the rapid pace. When they tire they hand the maul to someone else and the rhythm starts again.

When the groove is deep enough, six men raise one end of the rail above their shoulders and drop it on a short piece of rail. This breaks off the section of rail you need.

When the strikers backed off I reached for the maul of the man nearest me. Anderson, who was holding the cold set, smirked at me and said, "You better let one of the men take the hammer."

For answer I gave him a hard look and swung the maul, hitting the cold set dead on and hard. The other striker picked up my cue, and we struck a rhythmic pace. And I made damn sure I wasn't the first to back off. When I finally did, Anderson's smirk had changed to a grin.

The following morning Jude and I were plugging away at the holes when Anderson came and asked me my name. I told him and he repeated it as if filing it for future use.

"Mike needs two pairs of back spikers." They work in pairs, one man on each side of the rail. "Lindstrom's gang is on his tail, and he's going to be holding them up if he doesn't get more spikers. I know you can swing a maul good, but you're pretty young to keep it up for twelve hours. So don't be afraid to come and tell me if you find it too much for you. I'm taking the big Finn off the lining bar for your partner. He's worked for me before and he's a good spiker."

"Don't worry about me being able to tough it," I said. "I've spiked before and I know how to make the hammer do most of the work."

"That's good," he said. "Wait here until I get Sula. He's not gonna like it when I take away the lining bar and give him a spike maul, but I can't keep everybody happy and get the work done."

Four days after he handed me the spike maul we lost the super. He died on the job from a heart attack. It happened shortly after work began in the morning—the crew laying the steel had just thrown off the first rail. Because he was short-handed, Anderson was walking west on the track to put the warning flag out himself. He'd gone two hundred yards beyond the job when he heard the whistle blast of the approaching eastbound train. Without hesitation, he started running and frantically waving the red flag. Then suddenly he keeled over.

Ironically, there was no need for Anderson to run at all. The hogger had made many runs, both east and west, since the work began and was approaching with caution. Slow enough for him to stop when the engine reached the fallen Anderson. When he and the fireman couldn't revive Anderson they put him on the floor of the cab and brought him to where the gang was installing the switch-point.

Mike, the foreman, was up the track with the back spikers, and one of the gang ran and told him that Anderson had had a heart attack and passed away. "He's in the engine's cab now, and the hogger wants to know what to do with the body."

A startled Mike said, "Goddamned if I know. Drop your maul, Legs, run back to where Lindstrom's working and tell him what happened. He'll have to take charge of both gangs until we get another super, so he'd better make the decision about what to do with Anderson now."

Lindstrom was the super of a gang as large as Anderson's that worked a quarter of a mile behind. They changed the steel on one side of the track, while Anderson's crew did the other. I knew him by sight because his gandy cars were on the same siding as ours, and he always took his gas car off the track the same place Anderson did his.

I found him and said, "I'm from Anderson's crew. He had a heart attack and died a few minutes ago. Mike sent me to tell you."

"The poor bastard," he said. "I been expecting this to happen. He worked too hard. Two years ago he had a heart attack, and when he got better the railroad gave him a desk job. He hated it, but it was that or early retirement. His wife died seven months ago, and he was going to retire. But he took a physical and when he passed it he asked for his job back and got it. Now it's killed him."

I was starting to leave when Lindstrom said, "Wait. I'll take you back with me on the gas car."

The car was beside us and we could have put it on the track ourselves, but Lindstrom hailed two men who were heaving out the rail and told them to do it. I was struck by the contrast between Lindstrom and Anderson. They had equal authority but used it differently. Anderson motivated men by initiative and example, and his workers respected him for it. Lindstrom was aloof, and ruled by command. If he lived to be Anderson's age he'd be holding down an executive chair on the railroad board.

Things go unnoticed when you're not trying to get a reading on a man, but they swing into focus when you start putting the figures on him. During the week I worked for Anderson he always helped to put his car on or off the track, and I gave little thought to it. But when we got to where Mike was waiting, Lindstrom told Mike to get two men to take it off the tracks.

This wasn't a strike against Lindstrom, but as a young man trying to head in the right direction I felt I should put the figures on both to decide which I should follow.

Lindstrom had a few words with Mike and the engineer before he took charge. He had Anderson's body taken from the cab and put in an empty boxcar. He chose two old-timers who had worked several years for Anderson and told them to ride with the corpse. Then he followed the train with the gas car to transport them all back to camp.

For the three remaining days of that week Lindstrom took charge of both gangs. The following Monday, two new supers got off the morning train, one to take over Anderson's crew and one to replace

Lindstrom. Lindstrom got a boot in the ass up the ladder; he who was put in charge of the whole operation. We saw little of him after that because he converted Anderson's quarters into an office and ran the job from the seat of his pants. This gave me more fodder for thought.

Spiking becomes so automatic and routine you spend your days thinking and dreaming. After Anderson's death I spent three weeks doing both. My daydreams were mostly about farming. I owned my own land, developing it into a cultivated oasis, producing rich grain crops and prize livestock, with a loving wife and children to share the rewards. But serious thought always brought me back to reality. Where was I going to get land? So drop the dreams in the crapper, and stay with the railroad. Work hard like Lindstrom and Mike. They were working stiffs like me.

CHAPTER 24

I PUT THE FIGURES ON THE PAST FIVE MONTHS AND had them pretty well sorted out. All the pluses and minuses were ready for totaling when the clincher came. Mike came to me and said, "This job will wind up in another five weeks, but you'll not be out of work. The railroad is giving me a crew of my own. I'll be in charge of a rip-rapping job west of here. I'm going to pick my crew from this gang, but I'll only need about half of them. You'll have a job for the rest of the summer and all winter. By that time other jobs will be opened up and I'll get one and take you with me."

Environment is the main factor that shapes and dictates a man's lifestyle. But a chance happening at times overrides it, and there's no telling when or where it will strike. In my case it struck while I was having a crap, and it changed my mind about making the railroad my future.

Beside the camp they had the usual wooden six-holer with a six-foot galvanized piss trough. But if you had to use the crapper on the job you used the one nature provided: the bush or a field. Rather than use a handful of leaves or a tuft of grass, I made it a habit to fold a sheet of newspaper small enough to carry in my hip pocket. On the second of April I was hunkered in a field and about to tear the paper into little sheets when I noticed the heading of a small item: "Land open for homesteaders." It said that homestead land was being opened up in Saskatchewan north of Prince Albert.

Like a bigtime showoff lighting his cigar with a hundred-dollar bill, I had almost wiped my ass with a quarter section of land. I tore the item out of the paper and tucked it in my watch pocket. To hell with the railroad, I decided. Here was my chance to get land of my own. I never got a chance to tell Mike I was pulling the pin, but just before supper I went to Lindstrom's office and told him I was leaving after tomorrow's shift.

He tried to dissuade me. "Mike's very pleased with your work," he said. "There's a good future in railroading. For instance, Mike's only been with the road for two years and next month he'll have his own crew."

I didn't buy it. Instead, I pulled the clipping from my pocket and showed it to him. "I've always wanted land of my own," I said. "Now's my chance. I can't pass it up. If I did, no matter what happened, or how well I did with the railroad, I'd always look back and wonder."

"Well, think about it," he said. "And after you've slept on it, if you haven't changed your mind by tomorrow night, see the timekeeper. He'll get you squared up, and I'll give you a pass to Glendive. You'll have to go there to get your pay. But you'll maybe have to wait a couple of days for them to process it."

Four days later, knowing I'd have trouble proving to the Canadian officials that I was a Canuck, I waited until after dark before crossing the border. The next morning I got picked off a freight by two RCMP cops as it left the yards.

One was a snotty bastard who growled, "Where the 'ell you think you're going?"

"Saskatoon," I said, "I'm going home."

" 'Ome, 'ell! You're a bleedin' Yankee. You Yanks think you can come and go across the border any time you bloody well feel like it."

"Don't tell me I'm not a Canadian. You can't even speak like one. How long's it been since you crossed the pond? I'll bet you haven't been in this country two years, the way you talk."

"You cocky bastard. I believe you are a Canadian. You're cheeky enough to be one. You bloody colonials have no respect for authority."

"Forget that colonial shit," I blurted. "I don't have to take that from you. Don't tell me Canadians have no respect for authority. I respect the uniform you're wearing because it stands for dedication and tradition. But I don't respect the clown who's wearing it."

"I'm warning you," he fumed. "You better keep a civil tongue in your 'ead."

I clammed up, but not because I had shit up my neck. I had overcome the bull horrors before I was on the road three months. Yet I read the warning signs and knew it was time to lock my jaws.

They took me to their headquarters and let me sweat it out in a small room for half an hour before a corporal came in and fired questions at me about Saskatoon. When I answered them, he grinned. "You're Canadian all right. I went to the same school you did, and some of the same teachers taught us both. Kevin, the English constable, said you were very abusive when he questioned you. So I checked with the other officer, and he said Kevin only got what he asked for. Still, you were trespassing on railroad property." He let it sink in, then smiled. "But we're not going to charge you this time. I'm going to have a constable drive you out of town and put you on the road to Weyburn." I thanked him and shook his hand.

The cop that drove me to the outskirts was a good Joe. He fed me at a restaurant before we left, and when he dumped me, he said, "I'm letting you off here because we're only half a mile east of the railroad, and the grade there is so steep it slows the trains to a crawl. There'll be a train going north between three and four. It'll get you into Weyburn before you get too hungry."

Two days later I was in the government employment office in Saskatoon when a rangy, middle-aged farmer wearing overalls and a smock came in looking for a field hand. When I told him I was a field hand he looked me over and said, "You're big enough, but you don't look old enough to have much farm experience. How many horses have you driven at one time?"

That burned me up. "How many horses you got?" I snapped back. "Twelve is the most I ever drove at once, but I could drive more if the pay is right. I'm a long-line skinner. I've been driving horses ever since I was old enough to put my shoes on the right feet."

He smiled sheepishly and said, "I guess I asked for that. You won't have to drive more than six at a time. I pay the going wages, but I don't have a full summer's work. After the crop is in I can handle it all myself. I only farm one section of land."

"That's okay," I answered. "I'm going to file on a homestead north of Prince Albert in May, so that's as long as I want to work. How much is the going wage?"

"Sixty dollars a month and your keep, and you won't have to sleep in the barn. There's only the wife and I and we have three bedrooms. You got a name? Mine's Wilf Emerson."

I told him my moniker and took his outstretched hand. "Well," Wilf said to the clerk, "I guess that wraps it up. Ain't much use you filling out that paper now."

Then he turned to me and asked, "Where you got your clothes stowed? Go get them and meet me at Speer's Feed Store in half an hour. Do you know where that is?"

"Everything I got is on my back," I said, "except a change of socks, shirt and underwear. In fact I'm ready to go now as soon as I get the pack I stashed in the beanery next door."

I got my gear and waited in Wilf's 1925 Essex while he went to the bank, then bought seeds at Speer's. During the six-mile drive to the farm I gave my stock answers to the questions Wilf kept firing at me.

The Emerson's three-bedroom, two-story frame house and farm buildings were almost a quarter-mile from the concession road, up a lane flanked by Manitoba maples. Mrs. Emerson, a comely matron, was working in a flower bed in front of the house. She stood up, wiped her hands on her apron and came to greet us.

For the next few days, the land was still too wet to work, but Wilf and I kept busy getting ready for planting. We cleaned and pickled the seed grain, mended harness and checked and made minor repairs to the equipment. Since Wilf was solely a grain farmer there were no cowsheds or pigsties to muck out. He had sixteen head of good farm horses, and the biggest job was getting them ready for harness. Their shaggy winter coats had to be clipped, and we spent two days cranking the horse clippers. Then every horse had to have its hooves pared before it was able to walk all day without developing a limp.

When it came time to put a plow in the ground I had my pick of horses. I chose six evenly gaited horses to hitch to the plow. Wilf went with me to the field to help put up the strikeout stakes. He wanted to make the first round for me. I knew from the crooked rows of last year's stubble I could plow a straighter furrow than he could, but why make an issue of it? He was the boss, and he owned the land.

The day when I'd be able to file on the land was not far off, but it seemed like an eternity. Wilf was fortunate that my work never suffered, and it was a credit to the horses I was driving that it didn't. After you've hitched a well-trained horse to a plow or seed drill and started them down the field, you don't have to guide them. If you're plowing they follow the furrow, and if you're seeding grain they won't leave the wheel mark of the previous round. All you have to do is keep a tight rein on them and your eyes open. During the day, the only time I wasn't daydreaming was when I came to the head row at each end of the field.

Like the eve of execution for a condemned man it finally arrived. On the following day I'd file my claim. But unlike the doomed man who'd stop time if he could, I spent a restless night willing the clock ahead.

Finally Wilf tapped on my door and I crawled from the sheets. Wilf was on the kitchen porch with two lighted lanterns when I got there, and grinning like a schoolboy waiting for the bullfrog he'd put in the teacher's desk to jump out. "Good morning, Legs," he said. "Are you excited? But I shouldn't have to ask. I'm excited for you."

"Yeah," I said. "Excited enough I didn't sleep last night. But I'm still holding my water. I hope I cool down walking to Saskatoon."

"Walking, hell! You're not walking. I'm taking you. I might be of some help. I'm a property owner and you might need somebody to vouch for you at the registry office. We're well ahead with the seeding. Another ten or twelve days and the planting will be finished."

"I'm not much at thank yous," I said, "but I appreciate your help." After breakfast we went to the barn where we fed and curried the horses. Then I threw the harness on a team and hooked them to the stone boat. Finally, after we'd cleaned the stalls, I hauled the manure to the manure pile while Wilf watered the horses.

The only trouble I had at the registry office was signing the application for land transfer. My hands were shaking worse than a dog shitting cockleburrs. When the deputy registrar saw the way they were quivering, he put the papers aside, gave me a tailor-made and said, "Sit down and have a smoke. It'll calm you down. If you sign now, the way you are, your signature's going to look like hen scratches."

I took the smoke, thanked him and after several deep drags got control of myself. When I'd signed the papers, I asked, "When will I know whether I get the land or not?"

"It's yours now," he said, "but you got to prove it up. That shouldn't be a problem for you. Mr. Emerson tells me you're a hard worker and know how to farm. You got a strike on the city people that file for homesteads, but those that work hard do all right."

When we came out of the registrar's office, Wilf said, "You don't have to tell me you're a farmer now. I can tell by the look on your face. You're grinning like a moon-faced kid at a circus."

"Yeah, I got it. But I'm scared shitless for fear I won't be able to prove it up," I said.

"Don't worry about that. You got the edge on most homesteaders. At least you know how to farm, and you're not afraid of hard work. Come on, I'll buy you a dinner before we go home and tell Martha the good news. She'll be happy. In her own way the wife is quite fond of you, but she's the kind of woman that keeps her feelings under a blanket."

We met Martha in the kitchen and Wilf blurted out, "Legs got his land, and he's starting to worry already."

"And well he might!" she said. "Now he needs a woman to make a home for him. Men are like babies. They need a woman to look after them."

"You may be right," I smiled, "but first I have to prove up the homestead, and then I gotta grow some stubble on my chin. I'm too young to think of marriage."

"Nonsense," snorted Martha. "No man's ever too young for a good woman's guidance."

CHAPTER 25

I PUT THE LAST SEED IN THE GROUND ON THE SEVEN-
teenth of May, then brought the seed drill into the yard and parked
it beside the machine shed, where I unhitched the horses for the last
time.

They went to the horse trough and drank before clomping to
their stalls. After they were unharnessed and haltered, I led them
to the pasture and turned them loose. Watching them playfully kick
up their heels and roll on the ground reminded me of kids leaving
school for summer holidays.

I knew by the height of the sun it was noon and Wilf would be on
his way in from harrowing to water and feed his horses. So I went
to the barn to fill the mangers with hay and put a gallon of oats in
each oat box. By the time I finished, Wilf was in the yard unsnapping
the lines and taking the bridles off. I stayed in the barn and haltered
the horses when they came from the trough to their stalls.

As we were going to the house, Wilf said, "It's your big day, Legs.
I guess you figured it would never get here. The wife and I are sorry
to see you go."

"I don't like to leave, either," I said, "but I'm anxious to see my
land. I want to get started this afternoon if I can, so I'll leave right
after dinner. I'm a fast walker. I should make Saskatoon in an hour
and a half. If I get there early I might catch a train going to Prince
Albert late this afternoon."

"You won't have to walk if you leave after dinner. The mailman
goes by a few minutes after one. Hustle down to the mailbox and
wait for him. He heads back to Saskatoon from here, and he'll have
you there by two o'clock. But be sure and put the flag up, or he'll
go flying past if there's no mail for us."

The mailman dropped me off beside the CN yards in Saskatoon,
and I was on a freight for P.A. by four. I got a room on River Street
and hit the pad as soon as I finished putting the nose bag on. By five
the next morning I had eaten and was heel-and-toeing it to
Paddockwood. I walked until noon before catching a ride with a

young guy in a cordwood truck. He was dead-heading it from Prince Albert where he'd made an early-morning delivery, and we wheeled into Paddockwood in twenty minutes.

There was nowhere to eat, so I went to the general store and asked the clerk if there was a boardinghouse in town.

"No, I'm afraid not, son, there ain't much call for one. The town's not growed up yet, but it will. More people are settling here every year. Pretty soon there won't be no more open land left. What brings you here, anyway?"

"I came to see the homestead I filed on," I said. "Can you tell me who I see to find out where it is?"

"If you got your papers, Tod Morris can take you out and show you, but you'll have to go out to his place to see him. It ain't more'n a mile up the road. You can't miss it. His name's on the mailbox. He'll probably feed you when you get there, too."

"Thanks for the information," I said. "I came to the right man. But I better play it safe and fill up on cheese and crackers with a Coke to wash it down. I'll take it with me and eat while I walk."

The Morris house was two hundred yards from the road, and before I reached it four husky dogs came charging toward me. I would have turned tail, but I knew if I did they'd be more apt to attack. The long white fangs of the snarling dogs broke my stride, but fear forced me to shuffle on. The closer they got the more they growled, slowing me almost to a standstill. But I kept inching on, hoping desperately someone in the house would hear them. At last a voice yelled, "Blackie, Sarge, goddamn you! Come here!" The dogs stopped growling, turned tail and loped toward a huge man in a plaid shirt waving his arms as he ran toward us. Slowly, I followed. In the big man's presence the dogs ignored me, but I was still shaky when I reached him.

"Man, oh man," I said, "am I glad to see you. If you hadn't turned up when you did I'd have needed a change of underwear. I'm looking for Tod Morris. The man at the store said I'd find him here."

"He told you right. I'm Tod. I'm sorry about the dogs, but you can't keep them tied up all the time, and it's not often anybody comes here on foot. It's a good thing you didn't run, or they'd have chewed you up pretty bad before I got here. Now that you've found me, what do you want to see me about? You look too young to be a homesteader."

"Yeah, I know about dogs," I said. "I been around them all my life. You can't let them know you're afraid of them." Then I told him why I was there. "I filed on a homestead in the Paddockwood area, and the man in the general store said you could tell me where it is."

"That's right. If you got your papers, I'll know where it's at, and I'll take you there. It'll cost you eight bucks, though. If you're broke you can work it out at two bucks a day and your keep."

He looked at the papers and said, "Well, we'd best get started. It's nine miles from here and two miles in from the road. There's a trail going in, but you can't get a truck or car over it yet. They're working on it, though. It'll be open this fall. I guess you haven't ate since you left P.A. If you like, the missus will throw something together and you can eat while I saddle the horses. We'll ride, because if I take the truck we'll have a four-mile walk in and out, and I'm not in a walking mood today. You can ride a horse, can't you?"

"No problem. I was riding horses before I milked my first cow. Thanks for offering to feed me, but I bought a lunch at the store and ate it walking to your place."

There were two saddles and blankets slung over a rail near the stable door. Morris pointed to the smallest saddle and said, "Take that one. You'll have to adjust the stirrups, though. It's my daughter's, and her legs are a lot shorter than yours. Throw it on this roan mare. She hasn't been out of her stall for three days except to drink. She needs a run."

The little roan was so well gaited riding her was like rocking in a rocking chair. I hadn't been on a horse for so long I'd forgotten how pleasant it was. I was still enjoying the ride when Morris pulled up and said, "We're here. There's the stake marking the southeast corner of your land. I guess you'd like to look it over and see what you got. From here it looks like you got a lot of clearing to do, but

I know this quarter. I'd like to have it myself. This here's poplar country. There ain't much spruce or pine in these parts. But this quarter, and three others bordering it, have a strip of spruce and pine running through them. You got a lot of good timber, and that's something scarce around here."

We worked our way through the bush, ducking low-hanging branches, till we came to a wide creek. "That's another thing I like about this property," said Morris. "That creek never dries up. You'll never have to pump water for your stock, and it's damn good fishing most of the year." The trees had been burned off on the other side of the creek, and I judged by the new growth that the burn had passed through there about two years ago.

I pointed to the burned-over land. "I like that. There's not much clearing to do, except for a few large stumps to pull before the land is ready for the breaking plow. Is there anyone in these parts does breaking for hire?"

"Darcy Combs will do it for you. He's got a big steam outfit, so those stumps won't give him no problem. He won't even have to blast them. His big steamer'll snake them out like pulling tent pegs. I'd say if you got the money he'll break it for about twelve bucks an acre."

"I don't have any money now, but I will have by fall. If I can get a job around here I'll take it. If not, I'll go where I can. I've got almost half enough saved already."

"You won't have trouble finding work in these parts," Morris said. "It's hard to get men to come out here to work. They'd rather work where they can go to town Saturday night and have a drink and a woman. We're too far from P.A., and there's no place closer. When you get back to Paddockwood, go to the store and look on the notice board by the door. At this time of year there's always a job or two on it."

There were three notices on the board from farmers needing men. I read them all, then asked the storekeeper, who was stooped with age, "Can you tell me if any of these jobs are north of here? My place is seven miles north and two miles west of Tod Morris's place. I'd like to work as near my homestead as I can."

"Well," he said, scratching his bald head, "Mort Kramer's is the only one north of here. He's an American. A fine man. He settled here four years ago. Last year he married the school teacher. She's a local girl, finished school here, then went to Normal in Saskatoon and came back to teach here. You'll find him a good man to work for. He's got a phone. I'll ring him and you can talk to him yourself."

"Thanks. I appreciate your help," I said.

When I told Mort Kramer I was a farmhand looking for work, he said, "Fine. As soon as I milk the cows I'll come and get you. Put Horace back on the line and stay there. I only milk two cows so it won't take long."

Horace took the phone, and when he hung up, he said, "Mort says for me to give you your supper, and he'll be here by the time you're through eating." He rang his wife and told her to set another place at the table. Then he locked the store and took me to his home where I had a good meal. Horace and I were having an after-dinner smoke when Mort arrived. He was about my height but with a more rugged build. He looked to be in his late twenties, and I learned later that he was twenty-eight.

Horace looked insulted when Mort offered to pay for my meal. "You know damn well," said Horace, "that nobody in this part of the country would see a man go hungry. The wife and I were glad to feed this young fellow. Isn't that right, Jessie?"

Normally I don't like or dislike a man until I get the figures on him, but Mort gave me a positive reading when he treated me like a man and skipped the questions about why I wasn't going to school.

In the truck on the way to the farm he said, "You got a good pair of shoulders. I hope they're used to swinging an ax, because until haying time, that's what you and I will be doing. If you're not an ax man now, you will be by haying time. I got forty acres of poplar to clear, and every time I get a break from the land I hack away at it."

I didn't want to tell him that an ax was the first tool I ever used. So I tossed back an old cliché loggers use when talking to greenhorns. I said, "I'll do all right. At least I won't have to stand in a washtub when I'm chopping to keep from cutting my legs off."

The next morning I cut tree for tree with Mort, and we felled for an hour before stopping to roll a smoke. "Well," Mort said, "you sure don't need a washtub. I can hold my own with anyone when it comes to using an ax, and you been chasing the shit out of me for an hour. You handle an ax like you were born with one. We're going to make a hell of a dent in this bush by haying time if we keep going the way we are."

We spent three weeks on the forty acres, cutting and clearing before haying. Mort's farm had no hay on it, but there was lots of open land that did, and anyone was free to cut it. The only problem was that the nearest open land with a hay crop was three miles from Mort's farm, and we lost time going back and forth. But I didn't mind the extra hours we put in, because Mort and his wife, Nora, treated me as if I were a member of the family. On Sundays Nora would pack a lunch for me, and I'd saddle a horse and ride to my land and spend the day cutting brush.

At breakfast one Sunday, Nora said, "It's a beautiful morning, Mort. Why don't I pack a lunch for the three of us and we can ride out to Legs's place with him? One will have to ride bareback, but we can draw lots."

"I'm all for that," Mort said. "Legs tells me the creek there is teeming with jack fish and pickerel. We'll take some gear and get a feed of fresh fish for supper. But Legs and I will draw straws. You use your own saddle."

A few hours later when Mort and I were fishing across from the burn he said, "There's going to be a hell of a crop of blueberries on that burnt land. I'll have to bring Nora up here when they're ready. I guess from all the blueberry pie you've had since you've been with us, you know it's our favorite."

"Mine too," I said. "But as soon as I get enough money, I'm going to get that land broke. Tod Morris says I can have it done for twelve or thirteen dollars an acre. I want to get it done this summer and make a deal with someone to plant it next spring on a sharecrop basis."

"I'll make a deal with you now," Mort said. "If you don't leave when the harvest starts in the south, I'll let you bring an outfit up here when it's broken. You can disk it in two days. Then, when my crop's in next spring, I'll give you seed and loan you the horses and machines to plant it yourself. That way you won't have to share the crop with anyone."

And that's exactly what happened. I had the thirty acres of land broken, paid for and disked by harvest time. And still had a few bucks left in my kick. A week after freeze-up I pulled the pin. But before leaving I went to an auction with Mort and got a buy on a set of harness and a wagon I couldn't resist. Buying the wagon and harness put me in tap city again. I was on the bum once more. But what the hell, I'd head for Oregon and log till spring. Then I'd have a summer's stake and be finished with the road for life.

That was nearly seventy years ago, and I've logged countless miles since then. I'm an old man looking back down the decades, remembering the roads, the rails, the jungles, the jails, the railway bulls, the town clowns, the skid rows, the pool rooms, the greasy spoons, the camps, the gabfests, the blizzards, the sunsets, the whores, the lonely ladies and those migrant hobos I shared endless coffees with.

The roads and towns and railyards have all changed since then. But the people haven't. To me their faces are as vivid now as they were back then. They will live as long as I do.

I worked hard for four years to prove up the homestead, but the Depression did me in. I worked in mines, in factories, in logging camps, in carnies. I organized for the unions, carried a wobbly card, led some strikes and did time for doing it.

Other friends, other fights, other women, other years. Yet of them all, the thing I miss most is that lonely, distant whistle of a freight train in the night—gone now, forever, with the era of engines. But the places and people I've written about will live always in my memory.

For I knew them.

I knew them all.

Acknowledgments

I owe a debt of gratitude to many friends whose help and encouragement made this book become a reality.

To the Canada Council which, upon the recommendation of writers Paul King, Brian Vallee and Ron Base, gave me the grant that made it possible to continue writing, and to Jack McClelland who suggested that I apply in the first place. To the computer savant Murray Lamontagne, who made himself available day and night to exorcise the electronic demons which danced through my word processor. (Some of us might be better off with quill pens.) To Marion Cozak and Jean Surtees who typed the early versions of these memoirs. To Margaret Allen, my editor, who polished my narrative with craft and care. And especially to my friend Paul King, who kept me steadily on the track that led to this final destination: my hobo days contained between two covers.

And finally, to those forgotten men who once rode the rails beside me, and provided the stories told here.